8ᴅᴩ

THE BOYS' BOOK OF
ANGLING

D1614662

OTHER BOOKS AVAILABLE
Fancy Goldfish Culture
Frank W. Orme
Exhibition and Pet Rabbits
Meg Brown
Mother and Daughter Pony Book
Joan Shields
Bantams for Everyone
H. Easom Smith
Domesticated Ducks and Geese
Dr. J. Batty
Animals of the Countryside
Guy N. Smith
Modern Wildfowling
Eric Begbie
Elements of Shooting
R. Salisbury
Ratting and Rabbiting for Amateur Gamekeepers
Guy N. Smith

THE BOYS' BOOK OF ANGLING

BY

Major-General
R. N. STEWART

SAIGA PUBLISHING CO. LTD.,
1 Royal Parade, Hindhead, Surrey GU26 6TD

© Nino Stewart, 1980

This book is copyright and may not
be reproduced in whole or in part
(except for review) without the
express permission of the publishers
in writing.

First published 1955
Reprinted 1959
W. & R. Chambers Ltd.

New revised edition
Saiga Publishing 1980

Published by
SAIGA PUBLISHING CO. LTD.,
1 Royal Parade, Hindhead, Surrey GU26 6TD
England.

Printed and bound in Great Britain
at The Pitman Press, Bath

CONTENTS

THE
BOYS' BOOK OF ANGLING

Chapter I

HOW WE BEGAN

THE holidays started on the 20th July. My brother Ronald and I left King's Cross station by the night train. Ronald is thirteen years old and I am one year older.

To say that we were excited does not really describe what we felt. We were going to stay with Uncle Bob on the west coast of Scotland and he had promised us that we should learn to fish for salmon and trout. Not only that but he had told us that he had new rods, reels, lines and other tackle all ready and waiting for us.

We arrived in time for lunch next day.

After the meal Uncle Bob took us to the gun room and there on the dresser lay all the tackle. It was lovely.

" Now boys," he said. " These are good rods and reels; don't misuse them. If you look after them, they will last you a long time and, one day, you will be glad you took care of them."

I found out later that he had gone to Edinburgh and chosen the rods himself so as to be sure that they were " right " in every way.

" Now you have never caught a fish before, so you have a lot to learn," said Uncle. He then showed us how to put the rods up, how to keep the stoppers of the butt and middle joints, how to put on the reel and thread the line through the rings.

They were fine rods made of greenheart, with cork handles. They felt light yet supple, strong and springy. Uncle handled them and said, " Yes. Both will throw a fly nicely, but to begin with we won't teach you to cast a fly. I want you to catch a fish, so we'll just use a worm."

Ronald and I were desperately keen to go and try, and impatient to get to the water, but Uncle Bob insisted that we should learn how to soak our casts, tie them on to the line and tie the hook to the cast. All these things are very easy to do once you know how, but just at first they seem complicated and even more so if the mind is travelling ahead to the water.

Uncle said that lots of fish are lost by too much haste at the start and by neglect of these details. I expect he is right, as he is a very good fisherman and is now very old—a long way over forty—and has had plenty of time to learn.

" I have had some worms dug for you; but when these are done, you must dig your own, and don't let me find you uprooting my young celery plants or I'll be after you, and so will Archie." Archie is the old gardener.

" Why are the worms in moss?" asked Ronald.

" That's to scour them," said Uncle, " fresh worms are too soft and tender, and soon break up. After a day or so in damp moss they get tough and last much longer."

I think that they get tough by being hungry, because there does not seem to me to be much in damp moss for the worms to eat, but no one has ever really explained this to me.

A big burn runs close to the house. In it there are rocky pools, separated by shallow runs and little waterfalls. Some of the pools are quite deep, and the one near the stables is deep enough to drown in if you tried hard.

All three of us went together up the burn. " Here we are! Now Ronald, you're the youngest. You shall start here."

Uncle then took the hook on Ronald's cast and put on a worm.

" Now watch how I do it, as you'll have to bait your own hooks after this." He took a fat worm about an inch and a half long and ran the hook through it till it covered all the iron of the hook completely, and left a bit of its tail wriggling free. Then he took some line off the reel and dropped the worm and cast into the white water at the head of the pool, letting the line run through the rings meanwhile. "Now catch hold of the rod and let the worm run down the stream. You'll know when a fish takes it, because you will feel it nibbling, right down the rod and in the handle."

For a moment or two nothing much happened, then Ronald said:

"There's something at it." With that he gave a heave and out came the worm, cast and line away over his head and all got caught up in a tree behind him.

"Now," said Uncle, "there's no need to use all that strength. What you want to do is to pull the hook home in the fish's mouth and no more. If that had been a fish of any size, you would have either scared him so that he would not take again, or, if you'd hooked him, the cast would have snapped. Now go and get your tackle out of the tree and start again."

When Ronald had got his line clear of the tree, he began once more. "It's nibbling again. I feel it," he said.

"Wait then," said Uncle. "Count twenty and then tighten; don't jerk." When Ronald did tighten there was a little trout on the hook.

"All right! That's good," said Uncle, "but this one is too small. I know it's your first, but it's no bigger than the gold fish your aunt gave you last year. Not only that; it is very young and will grow bigger." So, wetting his hand, Uncle took the hook out of its mouth and put the fish back. Ronald was rather disappointed, but when Uncle went on to explain that all good fishermen want big fish and never, never, does a good angler kill a fish that he cannot use, Ronald was happy again. Certainly, this one was too small to eat.

" Don't worry! You'll soon get a better one," said Uncle.

I went to the next pool and spotted several trout in the shallow water at the tail of the pool, but they saw me and I did not need Uncle Bob to tell me that I had been stupid. In fact, I learnt then and there, that anglers should keep out of sight of the fish they wish to catch.

Uncle explained to me that the fish can hear and that if we make too much noise by stamping or jumping on the bank, the fish feel the tremor of the earth made by a heavy tread. Loud talking or shouting does not seem to disturb them, as the noise is not conveyed through the water. It seems that only noises that travel in the water are important.

" What about thunder?" asked Ronald.

" Now, that's a sensible question," said Uncle. " Yes; they do feel or hear thunder, and are very sensitive to it, but whether they hear the clap as we do, I don't know. I rather suspect they don't. What they possibly feel is the lessening of atmospheric pressure and possibly the electrical discharge which is released with all thunder-storms."

Just at that moment I caught my first fish. I had left the worm in the water and was listening to Uncle, so that it had plenty of time to swallow the worm. It was quite a good one. I tried to pull it out at once, but Uncle said, " Careful now; don't be too violent."

That fish pulled hard, but I managed to drag it over the stones and on to the grass. I thought it was huge but the verdict was, " No, not very big, but it will do." It weighed just six ounces on the kitchen scales.

We caught five that day which were keepable and, as we were going home, Uncle said, " Now that you have each caught a fish, I don't want you to think that all there is in fishing is to drop a worm in the pool and haul them out. If that were so, fishing would be a dull business. Every day you go out, there is something to learn, for me as much as for you. The fun is not just in catching the fish, but in finding out all about them, how they live, what they do, what they like, and a great many other details. Besides this, there are so many other wild things that live by the river and while you're fishing is a good time to learn something about them. So do not miss the opportunity."

" Can we go again to-morrow?" asked Ronald.

" Yes," laughed Uncle, " but you go alone to-morrow. I want to see what you can do by yourselves."

Chapter II

MORE OF THE BURN AND AN EEL

"WAKE up! It's eight o'clock," shouted Ronald. "Do you think I should go and dig some worms before breakfast?"

"Better not," I said. "You'll get all muddy and won't have time to wash again."

"Yes, I suppose you're right, but have we got enough?"

"Time enough to see after breakfast."

At breakfast Uncle said that we should try that bit of the burn which runs through the wood. He explained that there were some good pools there, but that we should have to be careful as the banks were very overgrown and the branches came down close to the water, so that if we did not take care we might break the rods.

As soon as breakfast was finished, we went to the garden and asked Archie where we could dig for worms. Archie is getting old and is rather slow. "Wurms," he said. "Weel now, ye can try the heap of muck at the back of the potting shed, but you'll need a fork."

"Won't a spade do?" I asked.

"Eh, and cut a' the wurms in half?"

We went to the " heap " at the potting shed.

" But this is only muck from the byre."

" 'Tis that, but it grows the verra best wurms," said Archie.

And that was very true, the first fork turned displayed worms in plenty, big, fat ones at that, and we soon filled our tins.

" Put a wee pickle of brick sand in wi' the moss," said Archie. " It scours them quicker." He showed us how to break up an old brick with a stone and " pepper the moss " as he called it.

Once in the wood we realized how right Uncle had been about the branches. I was afraid for my rod all the time, till I suddenly realized I was carrying it the wrong way, so I turned the butt forwards and held the point to the rear. This was much safer than any other way.

" Look Ronald, carry it this way," I cried, feeling rather pleased at having discovered something new and for myself.

The first pool we came to had one side free of trees and was fairly easy to get to and to fish. We caught one trout of cooking size in it. The next pool, which looked splendid, dark, deep and bubbly, was much more difficult. A hazel tree grew at the head and seemed to spread itself all over the pool. Ronald managed to drop a worm into the water between the branches and after a moment said, " I've got one," and with that he jerked the rod. Up flew the line, the cast and a trout on the end. The whole lot got hung up in the branches of that hazel tree. The trout was dangling over the water.

" What do I do now?" he asked.

" Get in the water or get out on the branch," I said. In the end the trout fell off and we recovered the tackle, but we so disturbed this pool in clearing the line, that it was no use fishing there any more.

On we went, to another bigger, deeper and rather sombre looking pool. This was well screened with branches, but not quite as inaccessible as the last one. I dropped my worm in at the top of it and no sooner was it well in, than I knew that it was taken. On lifting the rod, I felt at once that this fish was much bigger than any we had yet seen. It just would not come up, and I I had to give it line to prevent a break, much as I disliked it getting further away as I feared those overhanging branches.

" It's a whopper," I said.

" Be careful! You'll break the rod," said Ronald.

It was some time before I got it into some shallow water, but the moment it was there, Ronald threw himself on it, breaking the cast as he did so.

" You fool!" I said. " It's all right, I've got it," said Ronald. And he had, but in doing so he was soaked from chin to trousers. This fish was very ugly. It was black and had a huge head. We both felt that the catching of it was a triumph, and secretly, I think Ronald thought that he had been responsible.

As he was so wet, we went back to the house. On the way there we met Uncle. " What have you got there?" he asked. Proudly I showed him the fish and explained the adventures we had with it.

" Yes," he said, " there are bound to be a few big ones in the wood. You see no one ever fishes there, so they have a chance to grow, but this is an ugly brute, probably a cannibal, and well out of the water."

" It's a lovely fish," I said.

Uncle laughed, " It's a cannibal and eats its young, but go and weigh it, and you, Ronald, go and change." It was nearly two pounds, and I still think it was a grand fish.

After Ronald was changed we went out again. We had agreed to take pools in turn, as we found them, and I was fishing some way above him when I heard squeals. I was not sure that he had not fallen in again, so I went down stream to see, but no, he had caught an eel.

" Whatever shall I do?" he asked, " he's swallowed the hook, tied himself into dozens of knots and he won't keep still."

Ronald was by this time covered with eel slime, a peculiarly sticky stuff. Sure enough the hook seemed to be far down in its stomach. We banged

it on the head, but it would not die. In the end,
we cut the cast and took it home. On the way we
met Archie.

" Och the dirty thing!" he said. " Just cut its
head off!" And with that he produced a pruning
knife and decapitated the eel. Even after this
operation the body still wriggled and kept on tying
itself into knots.

When we got back to the house Uncle said, " If
you skin and stew it, an eel makes very good eating, but don't ask the cook to help you. She'll
only scream."

" How do you skin it?" I asked.

" Well, the books say that you peel it off like a
glove, but I never managed to do this, so you had
better find out for yourself," and with that rather
helpful suggestion he left us.

We tried hard to separate the body from the
skin but it was not a success, and in the end the
stable cat got the remains. I wonder why anyone
should want to skin an eel. All the other kinds of
fish are cooked in their skins.

Chapter III

ON COOKING LUNCHES
AND ANOTHER BURN

ON Sunday afternoon Uncle said, " Now come and see the river. We can't fish to-day, but you may as well see it and it's a nice walk." He went on to explain that when we were older and had learnt more, we should fish there. The river holds salmon and sea trout.

The pools looked so much bigger than those of the burn, which, of course, they were, and the water was deeper and the stream heavier. So big was it, that we were puzzled to see how we could ever get our worms out into the pools, so I asked Uncle.

" You won't fish with a worm there. You will have to learn to cast a fly. I have only started you on worms in the burn so that you may learn something of the ways of fish and how to manage for yourselves. As soon as you become good enough at that, then we'll teach you to cast." And with that we had, for the moment, to be content.

On the next day Uncle said, " Why not try the burn up the Glen. There are some good trout in it, but you'll have to take your lunch with you."

" Can't we cook our own lunch?" I asked.

" Yes, I suppose you can, but you had better go and ask Cook if she'll lend you a frying-pan."

When we asked Cook she was horrified, but soon she entered into the scheme with enthusiasm and loaded us with far more things than seemed necessary. She also put in some sandwiches, and a hunk of sticky, ginger cake, just in case our cooking was not a success.

Just as we were starting, Uncle said, " Got any matches?"

" Oh, dear! I've forgotten them," I said.

" Better take two boxes and a few dry sticks. It's been raining all night and I doubt if you'll find any dry wood to start your fire."

Soon after we'd started, Ronald stopped, went rather red and confessed, " I've forgotten the worms."

" You silly ass! You'd better go back and get them. I'll wait."

" Less of the ' silly ass '! If it had not been for Uncle, you'd have been without matches." He was already out of reach and it was not worth pursuing him for that remark.

When we got to the burn it was about 11.30.

" We will make our fire here," I said. " It's a nice, sheltered place."

" Would it not be better to catch some fish? I see no use for the fire if there's nothing to cook on it," said Ronald. " I don't fancy fried lard alone."

" Perhaps you're right for once. Let's go and fish."

We had nothing by 12.30 and it looked as if the sandwiches might come in useful after all. Then I caught a trout. " Hi, Ronald; come and clean this fish," I shouted.

" How do you do it?" he asked.

" Cut its tummy open with your knife and take the guts out."

" Lend me your knife. I've left mine at home."

" You'll forget your rod next time, I expect." With some reluctance I produced my knife. I had wanted to keep it clean.

Ronald cleaned the fish. Then he caught another quite good trout. By one o'clock we had something to cook.

" Can you light the fire?" asked Ronald.

" Of course! Go and collect some sticks." He came back with a bundle and we broke them into suitable sizes and put the dry kindling under them. The first dozen matches blew out in the breeze and before I knew what was happening, it seemed that nearly all the first box was empty. Ronald was laughing. " Don't you think it would be a good idea to collect all the matches you've wasted and make a little bonfire with them first?" He was right, but I did not want him to think he was too clever, so I asked, " Have you washed those fish yet?"

" Just going to."

At last the fire was alight. I put on the pan and melted some lard and in it we put those two trout. I expect that they were really a bit burnt, but to us they tasted delicious. We caught four more fish after lunch before starting for home.

Uncle Bob met us. " Have you cleaned the frying pan?" he asked, " because Cook will take a very poor view of a dirty pan."

" I washed it but the lard won't come off," I said.

" Try some sand and grass. That will get it clean. Do the same with the forks—that is if you used them and not your fingers."

Uncle was very particular about having everything clean. You see, he had been a soldier and had been on many expeditions in strange places and really did know what he was talking about.

Chapter IV

SOME THINGS ABOUT TACKLE

UP till now we had been very careful with our tackle, but, as we became used to fishing the burn, we began to lose hooks and casts in the stones and bushes. Also, when we got back to the house, we left the rods up, the casts on, and sometimes the worm remains on the hook. In the morning these had dried up into nasty hard lumps, making it difficult to rebait the hook with a fresh worm.

Then one day Uncle said, " That is no way to leave your things. When you come in, always clean your hooks, take off the casts and put them away in your cast cases." Then he went on to explain that daylight and sunshine is very bad for gut and soon rots it. He told us that one day we might hook a really good fish and lose it, because we had allowed the cast to rot. Not only the cast requires care but the line as well, and unless it is dried each day the dressing gets sticky and the silk rots. All that is needed is to pull the bit that has got wet off the reel and leave it to dry for the night.

" Where can I get some more hooks?" asked Ronald.

" Why? Have you lost them all?"

" Well not all, but I've only got two left."

" You can order them from the tackle maker, but you must buy your own from now on. Have you any pocket money left?"

" Yes, Uncle, I've 30p."

" You won't get many for that, so this time I'll see what can be done to help." He gave Ronald 50p. I had had hopes for some myself, but it was not suggested and I did not like to ask.

" Meanwhile," I said, " don't you dare pinch any of mine."

" Now, all good anglers give brother fishermen what they can, but I agree that they should not pinch without asking," said Uncle.

That evening Uncle gave us a tackle-maker's old catalogue. This was quite a big book and in its pages there seemed to be every conceivable device for the catching of fish.

" What a wonderful book," said Ronald.

" Yes, lots of people think that," laughed Uncle, " but don't buy all it offers to sell you, or believe all it says. Remember the tackle dealer is trying to catch the fishermen, not fish, so he makes the book look nice and makes you feel that you must have everything he has to sell; that's his business. There are other and better books on fishing. Look on those shelves over there."

" Good heavens! Are all those about fishing?" I asked.

" Yes and there are many more. You see it is a strange thing, but nearly every fisherman, after a time, thinks he will write a book about it. It does not do much harm to anyone and the author gets a lot of fun out of doing it. I don't know why fishermen get the urge to write, but they do."

" I shall write a book," said Ronald.

" That's grand," said Uncle, " but don't you think it would be a good thing to catch a few more fish first? At present, I doubt if you'll fill a postcard."

" Anyway you can't spell," I said.

"Oh! Uncle, have you ever written a book?" asked Ronald.

"I once tried," said Uncle.

"May we see it?"

"Well you can sometime," he replied, "but hadn't you better write for those hooks if you want to catch to-night's post?"

That night Uncle gave me a copy of his book and I took it to bed with me. I thought it was first rate. He seemed to have been in many different countries and this made it very interesting.

Next day we asked him to show us his tackle. He had dozens of rods and hundreds of flies, spoons, baits and other things. The room in which he kept them was like a museum.

"I'm not going to put up every rod for you two to flap about. It would take too long," said Uncle.

We asked him innumerable questions. He would reply, "That? Oh, yes! That was for salmon in British Columbia," or, "Now, that's what we used for cat fish in the Vardar, and this was for the trout in the Kura in the Caucasus," —and so on. In fact, it was almost a geography lesson and far better than a real one. Some of the things in the drawers were very old and had belonged to Great-Uncle Richard. "Why do you keep these old things if you never use them?" I asked.

"Well may you ask that," Uncle replied. "It is just the magpie habit. Some day I really must have a clear out."

"Oh! don't do that," said Ronald. "This room is such a lovely muddle. It would be a pity to spoil it."

"A lovely what? Young man, this room is the essence of orderly method—but perhaps there's too much in it."

Chapter V

WE LEARN TO CAST —TROLLING A FLY

WE had been fishing the two burns for about three weeks, when Uncle said it was time that we learnt to cast a fly. He went on to explain that the burn fishing was to give us a taste for the game and to find out if we would ever make real fishermen. He now thought that after some years we might. He went on, "But don't think you've learnt all there is to know about worm fishing, because you haven't. There are some forms of worm fishing that are far more difficult than fly fishing and which require greater control, more practice, knowledge and skill."

"But isn't it just putting the worm in front of the fish?" asked Ronald.

" It is just that," said Uncle, " but there are lots of places where that is not easy. Remember, it is the worm that matters; the less of the rest of the tackle the trout sees, the better. He must not see you, the rod, the line or anything which might arouse his distrust in your worm, but I'm not a worm fisher myself in the true sense of that art."

He told us that all kinds of genuine fishermen have their own methods and are entitled to the respect that is due to their skill. We were never to think that our own way was more sporting than any other man's. Each of us goes fishing for the sport and each man is entitled to fish as he sees fit, provided that his method does not spoil some-one else's sport.

" But why should it?" I asked.

" You will hear lots of people say that this or that method is spoiling the water. This is not always true, but there are some waters where only one method is best and where other methods do harm. Spinning in low, clear pools spoils them for fly fishing. Netting is a legal way of taking fish, but you would take a poor view of someone net-ting the pool ahead of you just as you were going to fish it. Fly fishing, to my way of thinking, is the best of all methods. Once you learn how, I hope you will use that method where the conditions are right. By doing so, I believe you will catch more fish, get more fun and never lay yourselves open to the accusation that your fishing has spoilt someone else's day. But, come on, we must be off to the loch!"

He had brought us to the loch to learn to cast as there was plenty of room and nothing to get caught up in. He told us that at first we would find it difficult and then said, " Watch me for a time and then try and copy my actions."

He took my rod and started to cast. The fly seemed to go out ever so far and just where he wanted it to go. It looked so easy.

" There are two things you must remember. Make the rod do the work, and, whenever you find things going wrong, try and imagine that the surface of the water is three feet higher than it really is."

We both started to cast. Some of our efforts were pitiable. Uncle kept up a sort of running commentary: " Now lift the line—give it time to straighten out behind you—not too quick—don't drop the point of your rod!"

We certainly learned something about casting that morning but our progress was very slow.

After lunch Uncle said, " Now there are some good trout here, and you are going to catch one. Remember these fish are much bigger than the trout you have been used to in the burn and you can't haul them out in the same way. When you hook one let it play. If it wants line let it have it. In the end the trout will tire and then you can reel it in close enough to use a landing net. Whatever you do, never try to lift a good fish out by the cast."

At this stage, however, he would not let us cast, as he said we were not good enough. He made us each let out about twenty yards of line and he slowly rowed the boat round with our flies trailing along behind.

It was Ronald who suddenly let out a yell: " I've got one." And sure enough he had a fish on. " John, reel up your line. Well done, Ronald! Now be careful! Give him line if he wants it."

Ronald did everything wrong in his excitement, but that fish was unlucky. It had so securely hooked itself that it could not get off. After what seemed to me ages, and longer to Ronald, Uncle was able to get the landing net under it and there in the boat was a lovely trout of 1½ lbs. Ronald was speechless with delight and so, I believe, was Uncle.

I did not hook a fish until it was just about time to go home.

Ronald could not go to sleep for a long time that night thinking of his fish, and, when he did, he dreamt of monster fish—or perhaps it was I that dreamt.

When Ronald woke up next morning he said, " We don't want to go to that silly little burn."

" Look here, Ronald," I said. " We're very lucky to have a burn to fish in. Uncle has been so good to us that it would be very ungrateful to say a thing like that."

" Yes, you're right," mused Ronald after thinking it over. " It would be a rotten thing to say to him."

Before the end of the holidays we caught several more fish and we could cast a fly, not very well, but well enough to deceive a few trout.

When we left, Uncle said, " Don't forget how to fish—and come back next year." He gave us each a book about fishing. " Don't believe all they say, but parts of both books are good and the tales of fish and their ways are always interesting. Remember that fishermen can't help writing and talking nonsense about their sport, and it is as well that they should."

Chapter VI

RONALD'S FIRST SALMON

DURING the winter all our plans were altered. We were to go and live with Uncle for some years, as Father had to go abroad and we had to stay at school. We went to Uncle at Christmas, but it was not till the spring that we were able to fish again.

That year Easter was late, but in spite of this,

the trout in the burn were still very thin. The food in a Highland burn does not hatch out into the stream much before April, and the fish had not had time to put on any fat.

Uncle said, " Of course they're hungry and easy to catch, but they aren't fit to eat, so don't kill any in poor condition."

It was during these holidays that Ronald, the lucky little beast, caught a salmon, so the tale must be told. Actually, I was very glad he had the chance and that all went well, but I would have liked to have caught one myself.

On that great day, Uncle was busy and he could not come with us, so Roderick, the head gillie, said, " Why not let the wee laddies have the day on the river? There are some fresh fish in."

" All right," said Uncle, " but mind they don't get into mischief; better take my old 12' rod and they can take turns with it."

This was a splendid idea. I wanted to take my own rod, but Rodrick said it was " too wee " and the reel did not hold enough line, so it had to be Uncle's rod, which seemed immensely long and heavy.

" There are still a lot of kelts about," said Roderick.

" What is a kelt?" I asked.

" A kelt is a salmon that has spawned and is on its way back to the sea. They're always hungry, puir things, and no wonder, seeing they've had nothing to eat for eight or nine months."

It is only a short way from the house to the river and we asked so many questions on the way that if it had been longer I think Roderick would have been sorry he suggested the idea of our coming.

The first pool is a big stretch of water with rushing, white foam at the top running out into a smooth, glassy tail. Roderick put on a very thick cast. He said that in the cold water of Spring you have to use big flies, so a fairly thick cast is necessary to balance the fly. The line too was about three times as heavy as our trout lines.

Then he chose a fly. It seemed to me rather like a small canary tied on a neat hook, but Roderick said, "Ay, there's nothing like a Yellow Torish," which was what the fly was called.

"What size is it?" I asked.

"About 5/o. Now just cast the fly across the stream and let it swing round. If you see a fish come to it, do nothing. Wait till you feel him, then tighten the line, but whatever you do give him time to take properly."

We both tried to cast the fly out to the places where Roderick said it should be and where the fish lay, but many of them were beyond our reach. We were not yet used to the heavier rod and the timing of casting with it. Places that we could not reach were fished by Roderick, but nothing happened at this pool.

The next pool was smaller and narrower. Ronald started. Roderick was telling him, " Now let the fly swing round, then leave it hanging— now lift and cast again."

Ronald did this three or four times. Then just as Roderick said " Lift——," Ronald said " Oh! look!" He did nothing, and there was a great boiling rise at the fly. It was as well that he was so startled as to do nothing, because a salmon takes so long to get the fly well into his mouth.

" My! You have him," exclaimed Roderick, and true enough the rod bent and there was Ronald with a fish on. I think that Roderick was nearly as surprised as Ronald was, but he would not admit it. All he said was, " Ay! That's a grand taking place."

Just at first neither Ronald nor the fish did anything. Personally, I am not sure which was the more amazed. Then the salmon went slowly off down stream and Ronald was obliged to follow, giving line as he went.

The fish went three quarters of-the way down the pool, then it suddenly turned and rushed upstream at an incredible rate. When it reached the white water it jumped. Even at this distance away it looked huge to me, and I am sure that to Ronald it looked far bigger. The reel made a screaming noise.

" Ay! It's a fish all right," said Roderick.

" Of course it's a fish," said Ronald. " What did you think it was?"

Then Roderick explained that the word " fish " only applied to fresh run salmon. " Kelts " were " Dirty kelts " or " them—things " and trout were " trouties ".

Meanwhile, Ronald's fish came back a bit and he was able to recover some line, but only a little. Then the fish gave two or three savage jerks which made the rod point dip and nearly jerked Ronald's shoulder out of joint. " Canny wi' him," said Roderick. After this it cruised round the pool for some minutes, sometimes taking line, sometimes coming back a little. During this time we never saw it. Indeed, apart from that jump, none of us had seen it. The salmon remained deep down in the heavy water.

Then it made a rush right to the tail of the pool and Roderick said, " I'm afraid he's for down," but for some reason unknown to us it hung on the lip of the tail and then came back, much to Roderick's relief. Ronald was too busy to mind much either way.

After some time the fish began to tire and we saw occasional glimpses of silver as it turned on its side in the current.

" Now bring him in slowly and quietly; don't jerk—no, not yet—don't worry yoursel'.

He's tiring. Just you stand where you are and bring him slowly to me," were some of Roderick's words of staccato advice.

Meanwhile, Roderick had taken the cork off the point of his gaff and crept down below Ronald, crouching like a sprinter at the start of a race. The fish came in slowly. Roderick reached out the gaff and buried the hook of it deep in the salmon's back and there it was kicking on the bank. A whack on the head and Roderick said, " Well I never—well done you."

Ronald was so delighted I believed he kissed that fish. It certainly was a lovely sight, a shiny rosy tint to it and sea lice on its back. It weighed twelve pounds.

Roderick took the fly from its mouth and said, " There's nothing like a Yellow Torish," and then, with great generosity, he took the fly off and gave it to Ronald saying, " You must keep the fly your first fish took."

" Oh! thanks awfully," said Ronald, " but are you sure you can spare it?"

" Why sir, I make them meself. Could I no be sparing one?"

We tried two more pools, but saw no other fish and then we went back to the house.

Ronald insisted on carrying the fish, much to Roderick's amusement, and took it right into Uncle's study.

" What!" said Uncle. " Did you catch that?

But don't put it down on my chair." It was some time before Ronald could be persuaded to take it to the larder.

Chapter VII

ABOUT KELTS—UNCLE CATCHES A BIG ONE

RONALD'S success made us both want to go to the river again. Uncle gave us leave to do this, but only when Roderick was available and when there were no grown-up guests fishing it.

But he said, "On the river you will find that you have many blank days, partly because you cannot cover the water and partly because salmon fishers often experience this. Indeed it is just as well, because if we all caught fish every day we went to the river, half the fun would have gone."

I am sure he was right, but our holidays were short and it would have been disappointing to have too many blank days. Ronald was lucky yesterday, but he might easily have fished for a fortnight and caught nothing. Quite apart from that, we did not have salmon tackle of our own and it was hardly fair to expect Uncle to keep us supplied, after all he had given us already.

I asked Uncle why salmon tackle has to be so different from ours. " There are several reasons," he said. " One is that in Spring the fly has to be bigger, because in the cold water the fish lie deeper and the fly has to sink down to them. They will not come up to a fly near the surface. A big fly requires heavier casts, and the line and rod have to be heavier to throw them. Then in the river the fish has more room, so the reel has to be bigger to hold sufficient line. Also, the lies of the fish may well be out of reach of a short rod. Your rods are quite strong enough to kill a salmon, though you might take a little longer to do it, and it would not hurt the rod, but, if you were to cast big 6/o flies with them, you would ruin the rod in a fortnight. Casting takes far more out of a rod than ever a fish does."

" I must save up and buy a salmon rod," said Ronald.

" That's a good mental resolve, but at the present rate of your income and the way you squander it, it will take some time," said Uncle.

" What are you going to do to-day?" I asked Uncle.

" I'm going to try the river. Want to come?"

" Yes, rather."

Uncle went off to put on his waders, long trousers, and he looked like a half-dressed diver when he was ready. It only wanted the helmet to complete the picture.

" I didn't have those things on yesterday," said Ronald.

" No, but Roderick only took you to places where you could reach the water without them. Now, you can carry the bag till we meet Roderick at the Bridge."

The Bridge Pool is long and wide below the bridge and to reach the best of the water it is essential to wade right in. The bottom is paved with large, round stones difficult to walk among, so Uncle took a wading stick. This stick has a sling on it so it can be slung over the shoulder. In this position it leaves both hands free for casting, yet the stick is there, handy when it's wanted.

I asked Roderick why a stick is necessary. " Well there's many a young man who'll say they are only for old men, but that's foolish. It's no use falling down at the beginning of the morning and wasting an hour of your time going back to change. Ay, sometimes a stick may save you worse than that, whatever your age may be."

I watched Uncle casting. There is no doubt that he is very good. The fly lands just where he wants it to and without any splash. He was fishing water thirty yards away just as easily as if it were half that distance. No effort seems to be used; the rod does all the work. He was wading in fast water up to his middle.

Roderick saw me watching Uncle and said, " Ay, he's a grand caster and he's just as good with a switch." Every now and again, Uncle made a switch cast. To do this he never lifted the line over his shoulder, but would draw the line clear of the water and up stream and then with a sort of swirly motion of the rod switch the line out. It was lovely to see it shoot out just as cleanly as if he had used the overhead method.

" Why is he casting like that?" I asked.

" Just for a change here, but there are places where the water can only be fished by a switch cast," said Roderick.

" Oh! look! He's got one!" shouted Ronald, and indeed Uncle had hooked a fish. There was the rod bending and Uncle turning slowly to come ashore. How slowly he seemed to move, but Roderick explained that it is better to come slowly and still have your fish on, than to hurry, fall down and lose it. Meanwhile, the fish was not doing very much, but Uncle had been very easy on it. Once he was ashore he made that rod bend till I thought something was bound to break.

None of us had seen the fish, but it still seemed very docile and it was slowly dropping down stream.

" I hae me doubts it's no a fish," said Roderick.

" Yes, I think it's a kelt. He's far too sluggish," replied Uncle.

After a time he got the fish into some slack water and we could see it. It looked to me to be huge. "Just an old kelt," said Roderick, and he put away the gaff. Uncle took it downstream to the shingle at the tail of the pool and gradually made it beach itself. Roderick walked up to it, lifted it by the tail and took the hook out.

"My, that fish would make 35 lbs. if he was fresh," said Roderick.

"Yes, he's been a big fish," said Uncle. "Before you put him back let the boys see him and show them his gills. They must learn to recognize a kelt." When Roderick lifted the gill cover, the gill was a sort of pale pink, not the brilliant dark red it should be; also there were maggots fixed to the gill rakers.

Kelts may be quite bright but somehow the silveryness looks hard and glittery and never has the rosy hue of a fish fresh from the sea. It is very easy to make a mistake and kill a well-mended kelt, and Uncle explained that lots of people do kill them. When Roderick put it back in the water, it swam away quite happily, almost as if it did not mind being caught. Still, I expect it was glad to get back.

"Always treat kelts well," said Uncle. "They've done their best for us and the river, and deserve good treatment. It always makes me angry to see a kelt mishandled."

"Do they come back again?"

"A few do, and for the most part only hen fish, but that's no reason to deny them the chance."

" How do you tell a hen from a cock?" I asked.

" By the shape of the head. A cock has a much bigger head than a hen and he develops a big hook on the end of his lower jaw. This ' neb ' as it is sometimes called, grows so big in old fish that very often they cannot close their mouths."

" Can you tell a cock trout in the same way?" I asked.

" Yes, but they do not have the same oversized neb. In the younger ones it is not easy, especially at the beginning of the season, as the growth of the lower jaw only becomes noticeable in the autumn."

Then Uncle went back into the river to fish.

" Look at yon Dipper," said Roderick. " He'll have a nest in that rock under the bridge." He pointed to the little, black bird with a white breast on a stone in the river. We watched him for a few moments. He was bobbing up and down just as if he was bowing to someone. Then he went into the water, dived and came up to bow again. " The little deevil; he's after the fry," exclaimed Roderick. The bird flew to the rock under the bridge. Ronald and I went there and sure enough there was the nest, very neatly made and roofed over like a wren's nest. We had some difficulty in getting to it as the rocks were wet and slippery, and the water under the bridge was fast and deep. I got there in the end and put a finger into the nest. There were two white eggs in it. Ronald wanted to take one, but we stopped him. Roderick said that Uncle would not like this, and went on to explain, " Though they do take a few fry, they do good as well. They eat a lot of elvers. Anything which takes elvers is a friend to the river."

" Do you know of many other nests?" asked Ronald.

" Ay! a few. You can't live by a river and not see plenty. There's so much to see by its banks besides fish, that I could write a book about it," said Roderick.

" Why don't you?" I asked.

" Mon, I'm no that educated, but I have it all in my head. Forty-five years on the river and you can see a lot in that time," mused Roderick.

Uncle did not move any other fish in that pool so we went on down the river. Here, he stood on a sort of pier made of big, rough, loose stones.

" Who made that pier?" I asked.

" That ' cruive ' you mean? Why I built it myself—carried all these big stones just as if they were babies."

" But what for?" asked Ronald.

" Well you see the river was spreading out just here and I made it to keep her in the right road, and well—it's done it. It's altered the stream and through time she has made a deep cut for herself and a fine lie for the fish to-day."

On the way home I asked Uncle if Roderick was a good fisherman. Uncle hesitated for a time before replying and then said, " On this river there is probably no one better. He has spent all his life on it and knows every stone, where the fish lie and just what to expect on each day of the season, but if you were to take him to a strange river I don't think he would be very good. He wouldn't be bad, but old gillies like Roderick who have been on one river for many years get set in their ways and find new conditions difficult. But you can learn a great deal from Roderick and he knows as much about this river as anyone does."

Chapter VIII

SPRING ON THE LOCH AND A CANNIBAL TROUT

IN the last week of the Easter holidays Uncle said we might try the hill lochs. " I do not think it will be much good. They are so high above sea level and the food for the trout does not hatch early in the cold water, but it's worth a trial. If you get any very thin fish, put them back. A month later would be better, but you'll be back at school by then."

It was a lovely, sunny day and Roderick came to row the boat for us. He was waiting by the boathouse. "It's a grand day, but I doubt if we'll get many trouties. They're no well awake yet," was his somewhat discouraging remark.

We started fishing and both tried to cast as far as we could reach, partly because we wanted to show off, and partly because of our days on the river, where we had to cast as far as we could reach.

"You're using too long a line, the two of you. There's no need for it; fifteen yards is enough and you'll catch more fish on a short line," said Roderick.

We were each using a cast with three flies on it: one at the tail and two droppers. "Your Uncle only fishes with one fly," said Roderick, "but I fancy it's better to give them a choice, though your Uncle catches as many, ay! and more than most folk, with his one fly."

Just then, while I was listening and looking at Roderick, I felt a tug, and turning, saw a good rise at my fly, but I was too late.

"There now!" said Roderick. "That's because you were no' paying attention. When your fly is on the water you must watch it, if you want to catch fish."

I cast again. I suppose that fish was very

hungry. He came again and I caught him. He looked lovely to me—something over a pound—but Roderick shook his head and said, "He's fat looking, but he's no' right. His stomach is bulging with food, but he's no' had time to get any fat from it. We'll just put him back. He'd be no good to eat—all soft and white." With that he dropped the fish back in the water. I felt rather disappointed, but I knew that Roderick was a better judge than I. A few minutes later I caught a smaller fish of about 12 oz. "Ay, that's better," said Roderick. "He'll do."

"Was that first fish a sort of kelt?" asked Ronald.

"Weel, you could call him that," said Roderick, "but he was better than that. Trouts don't have to go to the sea to get in condition like the salmon do, and you'll notice that their gills never go pale like the salmon kelts. That's because they can always get something to eat in the loch."

"What do they eat besides flies?"

"Shrimps, snails and bugs of all kinds. I mind once I was knocking a trout on the head and out of him jumped a wee frog and a newt. I fancy they would eat anything."

He went on to explain that the flies we were now using were very different from those required in the summer. These flies were bigger and very fat in the body. Roderick wanted them to sink deeper to look like nymphs and not flies.

At this time of year there are thousands of
nymphs in the water and the fish are looking for
them, but there are few flies hatched in April
1000 feet above sea level.

The way Roderick worked the boat was to put
it broadside to the wind and let it drift sideways.
At the end of the drift, he said, " Now put on
this big fly, let out plenty of line and troll it,
while I row slowly back, maybe you'll catch a
big one."

We had not gone far when I felt a tremendous
tug and the line fairly whizzed off the reel. Of
course the boat was going one way and the fish
the other, which made the line travel faster.
" Ay! that's him, the devil," laughed Roderick,
and he turned the boat to follow. It took some
time to get that fish under control and up to the
surface, and I must admit that towards the end
he was rather sluggish, but finally a horrible,
long, ugly fish came up.

" Careful now, we don't want to lose him,"
warned Roderick.

In lifting that fish to the surface, I felt that
everything was near the breaking point, but at
last his head was in the net. Most of his body was
out but we got him into the boat. As Roderick
knocked him on the head, a small half-digested
trout came out of his mouth.

" Oh! why did you kill him?" asked Ronald.
" He's much more of a kelt than the first one?"

"He's nothing but an old cannibal," said Roderick. "He eats young trout by the dozen. I don't know how old he is, but he's older than you are. Mind you, he's no good to eat, but I'll feed the dogs on him."

Roderick explained that these old trout never take a fly later in the season and only do so in the Spring because there is not yet much to eat in the loch.

"What will he weigh?" I asked.

"He should be well over six pounds if he was in condeetion, but he won't make much more than four."

The sun went in, the sky became overcast, and it turned much colder. "It's no use now," said Roderick. "At this time of the year, once the sun is off the water you can pack up; the fish just go down. If it was June and warm, I'd say it was just the time to start."

So we went home. However, we had at least one fish we could eat and one "well out" of the water.

When we got back I asked Uncle about fishing with one fly instead of three. "It's all a matter of choice," he said. "One famous old fisherman used nine, but I don't like the idea. The theory is that you fish the tail fly sunk and keep the droppers bobbing about near the surface. There are fishermen that can do this, and a lot more that think they can and don't. I like to control

my fly in the way I think it should work and I
find it quite enough to manage one properly,
but you must suit yourself in the matter. We all
fish to get fun out of it and if a multiplicity of
flies is fun to you, well, use them!"

Chapter IX

WE ARE ALLOWED TO USE THE
BOAT ALONE. FISH EARS. UNCLE'S
BIGGEST SALMON

WHEN the summer holidays started Uncle
asked, "Can you both swim yet?" We
had both been taught at school and were able
to reassure him.

"Good, then you can go out on the lochs
without Roderick, but, each time you take the
boat out, and put it back, everything must be
in its place and ship-shape. The oars and row-
locks, when not in use, live in the boathouse,
and are not to be left lying about on the shore.
The bailer is for bailing, not for cooking tea and
the boat has to be properly moored." We faith-
fully promised to attend to these details.

"Well, mind you do, because if I find any of
these things missing, broken or lost, then the boat
will be out of bounds."

The loch is not really very big and large parts of it are shallow. I do not think there was much risk of our drowning even if we had been stupid enough to fall overboard, or capsize the boat, but we felt that it was nice to be trusted to go there alone.

We were both learning some of the ways of trout and how to catch them, and it was now seldom that we came home " blank ". And we were not so extravagant with our tackle. Having to pay for it made a difference. But on the loch we were rather duffers.

One day when we came ashore for lunch we found Roderick smoking his pipe.

" What have you caught?" he asked.

" Nothing," I had to reply.

" I'm no' surprised, the way you set about it. Such a splashing of the oars and dancing in the boat would scare any fish out of the loch. And even if it doesn't do that, it tells them that yon two young fellows from the big house are out fishing the day. If you want to catch them you must creep about on the water as if you were stalking a rabbit." He was right, of course, and once we rowed quietly we caught more fish.

I asked Uncle about it and he explained that fish not only see but hear as well. They do this by means of the nerves of the lateral line which act rather like ears. They record all water vibrations, which are like noises to the fish. Therefore, if an

unusual one is felt, they know that something odd
is happening. No wonder then, that an oar splashing puts them off.

"What were the trout eating to-day?" asked
Uncle.

"I caught mine on a Zulu," I replied.

"I did not ask you what you caught your fish
on, but what food are they taking just now."

"I don't know," I replied.

"Well, go and look," said Uncle.

"How?" I asked.

"Cut its stomach open and see," laughed
Uncle. This idea had not occurred to me before.
It was rather a messy job and in the stomach
some of the things are not easily identified, but I
saw snails, shrimps, some flies and what looked
like a beetle. But Uncle's idea certainly was a good
one.

Two or three days later I had a run of bad luck
and lost several good fish when they rose, and,
what was worse, lost several flies in fish. When I
told Uncle all he said was " Bad luck! nonsense,
bad knot tying is the right word. Show me how
you tie on a fly."

When I had done this he took the fly and cast
and pulled, off it came.

"Now look!" he said. " If your cast is a gut
one a ' double sheet bend ' on an eyed fly is a
secure knot. After all it will hold a battleship so
it should hold a trout. If, however, the cast is

nylon, it is better to put a thumb knot on the end of the cast after it is through the eye, then make the double sheet bend, pull the end with the thumb knot till it is close up to the bend, cut off the spare piece. With the thumb knot a single sheet bend will do for very small flies. There's an awful lot of nonsense talked about knots and the variations of them are almost unlimited. Some are good, others are so complicated that I've never tried to learn them. They seem to have more turns than there are in any corkscrew."

" What knot do you use for tying the cast to the line?"

" A figure of eight knot. All it is is a reef knot with the end turned round the line and tucked into the loop of the reef. I use this for gut-eyed flies if I have them, but gut eyes are out of date and a good job too. They were responsible for many a lost fish, because the gut perishes and the eye breaks."

" Why, all those knots are in the Boy Scout books," said Ronald.

" Of course they are! Those books are very sensible. But there is one knot you should know which I have never seen in them; that is the blood knot for tying two pieces of gut together. But, here is a little book which describes it, *Fishermen's Knots and Wrinkles*. It only takes a few minutes to read, and if you learn the knots in it you will not want any others."

" What's the biggest salmon you've ever caught?" asked Ronald.

" Thirty-four pounds," said Uncle.

" Tell us about it."

Uncle laughed. " There's not much to tell, but it was a good fish. It was on the Spey on the opening day of that season. The weather was bitterly cold with a strong north-east wind and showers of sleet and snow. I started fishing at about 10.30 a.m. and by 3 p.m. all I had done was to catch seven kelts. I was using a 7/o fly and a heavy, fourteen foot rod and was getting cold, tired, wet and rather miserable, so I said to myself, ' I will have ten more casts and then go home.' A fire and a hot drink seemed more attractive than shivering on that river bank. I do not remember now how many of the ten casts I had made, when a fish took the fly. I did not see him. Those big flies sink down deep and you are often only aware of the rise when you feel the pull. So it was with this fish.

" ' Another kelt,' I thought. However, he seemed more lively, and as I was getting to the bank, he rushed upstream. Now, kelts do not often do this in strong running water such as this was. Anyway, he went on running. Out went all the line; the backing followed till I thought nothing would stop him. The gillie kept saying, ' He'll turn ' but I began to doubt if he'd turn soon enough. However, the gillie was right. He did turn, but only just in time. I don't believe I had ten more yards of backing left on the reel and there were over a hundred yards of it to start with, besides forty yards of casting line. After he turned, I got some line back, and about half of the backing, but he stopped about 90 yards away. The Spey is a big river and in a spring spate it is easy enough for a fish to be 90 yards away from the angler. However in the end I got him into some slack water and the gillie made a super job of the gaffing. He was a lovely fish. Of course by the standards of big salmon, he was not a very large one, but he fought as well as any salmon I can remember."

" Why did you not have it stuffed?" I asked.

" Stuffed fish are monstrosities," said Uncle. " The man who catches a good fish will remember it well enough without having its body collecting dust on the wall and no one else ever wants to see the thing. They are merely a nuisance to your heirs when you die."

" You could have given it to a museum."

" Most museums have more stuffed fish than they want already. No; don't stuff them. Eat them. If you want a record of a particular fish take a photograph of it. That, at least, does not take up much room, and it burns easily when your executors have to clear up your estate."

Blood knot

One-half double blood knot

Knot used for fastening line to cast

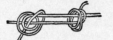

Double fisherman's bend, used sometimes instead of blood knot

Chitty's slip knot

Cairnton knot for joining cast to fly

Double sheet bend

Figure-of-eight knot

Whip finish

How to deal with a difficult joint with pliers and emery cloth

Cane splints

Cane Splints bound over fracture

FIRST AID FOR ROD FRACTURES

The 'OTTER'

Hand-made fish carrier

Chapter X

SEA TROUT BY DAY AND BY NIGHT

IT was in these holidays that we started fishing for sea trout. There is a very good run of these fish in Uncle's river. They begin to come in from the sea in early July, though there is an earlier run in June.

We had been given some sea trout flies and the first day we went to try for them the river was just running down after a night of heavy rain— one of those days when everything was sparkling with fresh raindrops shining in the sunlight.

Roderick met us at the Bridge. He had with him the longest landing net I have ever seen. I asked him if such a weapon was necessary. " No," he said, " but I made it myself and I've got used to it. Sometimes it's handy enough to have two feet extra on the end."

We started fishing at the Bridge pool, Ronald at the top and I about half-way down. Roderick sat on a stone somewhere between us and smoked a pipe. He said this was to keep the midges away and, judging by the smell of the smoke, you would have thought that no midge could survive within a mile of it. However, he seemed to enjoy it.

Before we started, Roderick said, " Now, you

mind how I told you to fish the fly for a salmon? Well, where there's plenty of stream you do just the same for sea trout. Just cast across and let the fly swim down and round; but once you get to the stiller water you must give the fly some motion to make it look alive, just as you do in the lochan, and don't stay too long in one place."

Soon after he had started Ronald gave a cry of distress, a fish rose to his fly, gave it a fierce tug but failed to get hooked.

" That's because you were not paying attention. When you're after sea trout you must watch your fly all the time it's on the water and no' be gooping at other things," said Roderick.

" But I only looked away for a moment," said Ronald excusing himself.

" I know. And that's just the moment the trout came to the fly."

Then I hooked one. This fish more than surprised me. I had caught quite a number of trout but they never behaved as madly as did this sea trout. It ran, it jumped, and it ran again; it gigged, jerked, splashed and never for a moment did it stop. Roderick came up with his gigantic net and with a sudden swoop he had it. Just at that moment the fly came out of its mouth. However, it was safe in the net.

" Well done, but I'm thinking there's some use in the long handled net after all," laughed Roderick, and indeed he was right. If we had had to wait till it was close enough for a short one I would have lost that fish.

When I was playing that trout it felt enormous, but when weighed it was only a little over a pound.

" How does a fish of that size put up such a fight?" I asked.

" Well they're strong just coming from the sea. Now go and get another, there's plenty more there."

Ronald caught a little one about half a pound. " They're grand eating are ' finnock '," said Roderick, " but never take more than you want for the larder as they're just babies and will grow bigger."

" What are the best flies for sea trout?" I asked.

" No man can tell you that, but there's many a man will tell you what he thinks is the best fly and in the end the fish will think it right too. One man with one kind of fly that he keeps on the water, will catch more fish than another man with three dozen flies in his box."

" Uncle told me to put on a Peter Ross," I said.

" Ay, it's a favourite fly of your uncle's and he's a grand fisher. We can both tell you a lot about fishing, but neither he nor I can make a fisher of you. You can only do that yourself. As I told you before, the man who catches the most fish is the man who keeps his fly longest on the water where the fish are. Ay, we can tell where to fish and what to fish with, but it's you that have to do it," mused Roderick.

Ronald and I were both enchanted with sea trout and when we got back for tea Uncle said he had never seen two such keen anglers. " As you are so enthusiastic you shall have a treat to-night. We'll go out after dinner to the House pool and see if you can catch a big one."

" Why after dinner?" asked Ronald.

" That would take a better man than me to explain," he said, " I don't know why the big trout take better at night, but they do. It's best on a still, warm evening and to-day the conditions are about right. Anyway, we'll see."

Ronald and I gobbled our dinner and showed other signs of impatience till Uncle said, " There's no need to hurry. The light is not going yet and we may as well sit here and eat in comfort, rather than sit on the bank and be eaten by midges."

This of course is the kind of reply an elderly person would make, and, even though it is the right answer, we both felt that every moment we sat there we were missing fish.

However at last Uncle said, "Well, let's go. Have you got a torch? Better take one; it's sometimes useful." On the way to the river he explained that it is better to use rather bigger flies in the dusk and bigger still when the light goes, also it is better not to move away from a good place once you have found one, as the fish move in to these places at night.

When we came to the river he approved our

flies and gave us each a section of the pool to fish and he went up the river to another pool.

The light was beginning to fade as we started to fish. As it got darker, I had expected that it would not be easy to see where I was casting, but, even on darkish nights when the sky is clear, there is a certain amount of light at this summer season in Scotland and the eyes get used to it. There was no difficulty.

I had not been fishing long before the midges found out that I was there. They can be bad enough by day, but in the dark, they seem to be ten times worse, ten times as hungry and a hundred times more numerous.

I was frantically wiping midges from my face when my fly was taken by a fish. I did not see the rise and as soon as I tightened on him he was off like a rocket. I could feel that he was a big one. Then he jumped, and Oh! what a splash he made, but it was too dark to see the fish clearly even when he jumped. He went up, down, across and towards me. I never knew where he was or where he would go to next moment. Both hands were fully occupied and it was this moment that the midges made their fiercest assault. It seemed as if all the midges in Scotland were saying, " Now he can't defend himself! Let's feed." I do not know how long it took to play that fish, but in the end I got it into the landing net. It was too big to lift so I dragged it on to the bank.

I've seldom seen a lovelier fish. It was fat and thick and shining like a new shilling. After I had disposed of it I had a glorious scratch. As soon as I started again, I hooked another trout at once, not so big this time, but just as lively. I lost count of the number of times he jumped and I did not take so long to land it. He was just as beautiful as the first one. As I was taking the fly out of his mouth I heard frantic yells from Ronald down below where I was. So I went to see what trouble he was in. He was standing on a stone some way out from the shore with a fish on. " Oh! he's stuck in something! I can't get him to move and he's very big," wailed Ronald.

" Are you sure it's not the bottom you've hooked?"

" No, no," he said, but I had some doubts, so I waded in to see. His line disappeared about five yards away into the black-looking water. However, it was not deep there so I took the net and went out to where it seemed to be stuck.

" Don't pull at all just now," I said, " and if I want more line give it to me." I managed to get near enough to see that his line was round a dead branch on the bottom. How I managed to get it clear I still do not know, but I did. " Now, reel up," I shouted to him, but alas! the fish had got off. " Never mind. You'll get another one," I said to console him, but Ronald was very quiet and I knew that he felt the loss of that fish bitterly.

However, I got him started again and I was just going back to fish my bit of water when he cried, " I've got one." This was not yet quite a true statement, because the fish was very much alive, a long way out and only rather doubtfully connected to Ronald. So I stayed to help.. This fish behaved differently than had my two and he was not so lively. " Is he a big one?" I asked.

" He feels enormous," said Ronald, " and he just goes where he likes and I can't stop him, nor can I hurry him, but Oh! the midges."

I had both hands free to deal with midges and I went to Ronald and was able to drive a few of his away.

I suppose he had had that fish on for about six minutes—it seemed like an hour to Ronald—when all of a sudden it went mad and rushed upstream till nearly all the line was out. " What shall I do?" moaned Ronald. " Follow him quickly," I shouted. Then the fish jumped and the splash told me that Ronald was right and he had a big one on.

We went up stream as fast as we could stumble. We had to be careful as it would never do to fall. It was fairly dark by now and there were big boulders and holes which were not easy to see. Meanwhile a mist started rising from the river making it more difficult to judge even the approximate position of the fish.

This trout went up to within a few yards of

where I had left my rod and at that moment Uncle appeared. " Hallo!" he said. " What have you got on?"

" It's a whale of a fish," said Ronald.

" Well, it's a very big one," I granted.

Now that Uncle was there, our confidence returned and we all felt that Ronald was going to win this battle. But that fish was still very active and kicking up a tremendous commotion some way out.

" Yes. By the sound of him he's a good big fish," said Uncle; " how long have you had him on?"

" All night. And my left arm is nearly dead."

" He's had it on for about twenty minutes," I said, and I think I was better able to judge the time as my arm was not aching.

" Stick it boy, you'll get him," encouraged Uncle.

It was some time before that fish began to tire and, even when he did, it was very difficult for Ronald to drag him near enough to use the net. Uncle knew just where he would and could be brought in and was there with his net, which was bigger than either Ronald's or mine. I must say that Ronald managed very well. He had to bring the fish in three or four times, but each time he got it nearer to Uncle. Then in the dim light I saw Uncle stoop down and he got the head of the fish into the net and dragged it ashore.

" Well done Ronald!" he said. " This is a
grand fish." And indeed it was. I had thought
mine was a whopper but this one was far
bigger.

After we had told Uncle all about what we had
done, and I had shown him my two fish, he said,
" We'd better go home now."

" Oh! Why?" asked Ronald.

" When you see that white mist coming off the
river it's no more use. You hooked that fish just
before it started, didn't you?"

" Yes," said Ronald, and indeed the mist was
now almost a thick fog. Also, Ronald and I were
both very wet and if we were not to catch chills,
it was time for us to change.

" What causes that mist?" I asked.

" It comes after a hot day, when the evening
air gets cooled to a certain temperature a form of
condensation takes place and water droplets form,
making the mist. It's just like a fog in England."

When we got back to the house the fish were
weighed. Ronald's was $7\frac{1}{2}$ lbs., mine $5\frac{1}{2}$ and $2\frac{1}{2}$ lbs.
Uncle had none. I know now that he gave us the
two best places.

" Uncle, that was a perfect evening," said
Ronald. It was midnight before we were in bed.
" Ronald," I said. " We must do that again."

Chapter XI

SOME NEW METHODS ON THE BURN

" GOOD morning, Uncle! Can we go out to-night again?" Uncle laughed. "We'll see," he said, " but you can't go out every night and lose all that sleep at your ages."

" But if we don't go out I shan't sleep for thinking about it," said Ronald.

" And anyway we don't know what it will be like to-night. At present there is far too much wind and the glass is falling. However, we'll see."

" Ronald, why don't you go to the burn this morning?" I asked.

" Go to the burn and catch those little tiddlers?" Both Uncle and I laughed. It was clear that Ronald now only thought in terms of seven pounders.

" You know you should not despise the burn, Ronald. After all, it was there that you learnt to fish and just because you've caught one big trout, the burn is still worthy of your attention. I have caught a great many big fish, but I still enjoy burns," Uncle said.

" Yes, that was a stupid thing to say. I do love the burn and its trout, though I wish they were a bit bigger."

" You know even small burns sometimes hold surprises," Uncle said. " I remember, when I was about your age, my grandmother took me to a burn which ran by the stables and told me she wanted to see me catch a fish. I did not have great hopes, but I had faith in her.

" There was a deep pool where an old saw-mill wheel had made a hole, so I dropped my worm in there, still rather doubtful that anything would take it. Then I lifted the rod and was fast in a whopper. Quite how I got it on to the bank without breaking the rod or cast I don't know. Then Grandma came to the rescue. The fish was jumping about on the edge of the burn and likely enough to slip back into it, when she came and sat on it. In those days elderly ladies wore long, sweeping skirts, many petticoats and I don't know what else. All these garments swept the ground. Well, she smothered that fish and we had some difficulty in finding it among all the garments she was wearing. I thought it was splendid of her at the time, but as I grow older I think her action was even more gallant, as she must have detested the idea of getting all those innumerable frills covered with fish slime and remains of worm. That fish weighed $2\frac{1}{2}$ lbs. I can see the old dear now, just as if it was yesterday."

" Have you got any worms, Ronald?" I asked.

" No."

"Come on then," said Uncle. "Let's all go and get some."

I think he was inspired by the memory of his tale, but he also wanted to maintain our enthusiasm. Anyway, we went off to the midden heap to get some worms.

When we came to the burn, Uncle told us about the upstream method of worm fishing. "I'm not much good at this, but here is the way it is done. Ronald, give me your rod and I'll try and show you." He stood below a fast and rather shallow pool and gently cast the worm to the top of the pool. Then by some magic he kept the worm gently rolling down towards him. All the time he seemed to be in touch with it. After the third cast he caught a trout, quite a good one and neither Ronald nor I had ever expected to see a good fish there. It was then I realized I still had a lot to learn.

"It's not only in the deep pools you'll find them. There's plenty of sizeable trout in the fast runs and this is the way to catch them," said Uncle.

"But how do you keep control of the worm and line?" I asked.

"It's just a matter of practice. After a few days you'll be much better at it than I am," he said.

We had not been out very long when a man came to see Uncle and he had to leave us, so we went on alone. The worms we had were not toughened and very soon they were all used up.

" I'm going to try a fly," I said, and it was not very long before I got a fish, but I found that this casting on the pools of the burn was many times more difficult than on the loch or river. There seemed so little water on which to place the fly, but clearly it was good practice. It did not take either of us long to become fairly accurate and to put our flies in the right place three times out of five, which I thought fairly good.

But a day or two later when I told Roderick how good I was, he laughed. " Any man that canna put his fly on a soup plate at 20 yards, canna cast." I think that this was a bit of an exaggeration, and he just wanted to impress us, but I must say he was very good. We gave him various targets to cast at, such as big bubbles and floating foam, and he generally hit them or was very close to them.

That afternoon the weather turned to wind and rain, so there was no use in thinking about going out after dinner and we had to be content listening to Uncle. We were well entertained, because some of his stories were great fun.

The rain was very heavy at bed time and the last thing I said to Ronald was that it would be a big river in the morning.

Chapter XII

FISHING THE RIVER IN A SPATE. MY FIRST SALMON

IT was a stormy morning. The rain was coming down as if it would never stop. Roderick came up to the house and Uncle said, " Take these boys and get a salmon amongst the three of you."

" The river's rising yet; I doubt if it's likely we'll be getting a fish. However, we can try," was Roderick's reply.

So off we went armed with two old salmon rods and muffled up in oilskins and rubber boots.

The river was very dirty, quite unlike the nice clean stream of two days ago, full of mud, sticks and other flotsam.

Roderick explained that in a spate like this the salmon come into the quiet places as the current in their usual lies is far too swift to be comfortable for them. He went on, " You see, salmon are not unlike ourselves; they like peace and quiet. We'll just be fishing the backwaters, but if you do get hold of a fish, he'll be off into the stream and who knows where he'll stop?"

" But you said it was no good," said Ronald.

" Ay! maybe I did, but I'm no' a salmon and there's no telling what a salmon might do, so when you're fishing just keep your eye on the water as if you expected him at any moment."

Well, we fished all morning and beyond a finnock, caught by Ronald, we saw and caught nothing else.

About midday it stopped raining and there was a break in the clouds. " If there's no more rain she should fine down by four o'clock and then there'll be a chance," said Roderick.

It was just as Roderick foresaw. The river became clearer and the height began to fall soon after 3 p.m. At each pool we visited, Roderick had put a little stick just at the water's edge, and when we came back to the Bridge pool at 4 p.m., the water had fallen at least an inch.

" A big Black Fairy is the thing they'll want here," said Roderick.

At first I thought that he meant to please the real fairies, as I am sure he believes in them, but he produced an old tobacco tin from his pocket and from it a large blackish and rather sombre fly.

I must say that it did not look very attractive to me. Obviously it was old, the hook was rusty, but Roderick explained that often an old, worn fly is more attractive to the fish than is a shiny, new one from the shop. This black monstrosity was put on.

" Now you see yon swirl in the water," said Roderick pointing to the spot. " Well, just by that is where he'll take you."

I started casting some few yards above the swirl and slowly worked towards it. The nearer I got the more excited I felt. Just when the fly swam past the swirl, a salmon came up and made a lovely rise to it. I was so excited I struck at once.

"Ay man, you just pulled it away from him. However, never mind; he has not touched it and I think he'll come again," said Roderick.

He insisted that we should wait five minutes before trying that fish again. It seemed an awful long five minutes to me and I can't say that I was any less excited when I began again, but I was determined that, whatever I did, I would not snatch it away from the fish a second time. Sure enough he rose once more and I did nothing. For a long time my heart was in my boots, because I thought he had missed it or refused it, but after what seemed ages I felt a pull. I lifted the rod and the line tightened and the fish was on.

"That's fine," said Roderick. The fish at first seemed rather dull. I suppose that I was so used to the jumps and rushes of trout and sea trout that I expected something of the same liveliness from a salmon, though on a grander scale.

For some time he cruised around slowly as if rather muddled as to what he should do, then he was off with a mighty rush and I had no further reason to complain of inactivity. He took yards and yards of line and I thought he was never going to stop. " Roderick," I shouted. " Will he ever stop?"

" He's all right. He'll come back soon," was his reply, which showed a confidence I was far from feeling. However, the fish did turn and in the end we caught him. I do not know just how Roderick managed to gaff that fish. Showing a vigour that I did not think he possessed, he suddenly produced the gaff, plunged it deep into the water and there, on the bank, was the fish.

However I did not stop to ask him about it at the time, as I was far too excited at seeing the fish on the shore. After all it was my first salmon.

" How big is he?" I asked. " He must be twenty pounds."

" Maybe he'll make fifteen," was Roderick's rather cautious reply. Actually that was its weight according to the spring balance. Even to-day I think that that balance weighed light, and I still think spring balances are soulless pieces of machinery.

" Now try again! There's more fish in this pool," encouraged Roderick.

" Shall I start at the top again?" I asked.

" Yes, come down it again just as you did before."

" Where will one be likely to come this time?"

" In the same place and from then on down to that big stone on the far bank."

I started again at the top and once again I felt that rise of excitement as the fly neared the swirl, but nothing happened and it was not till the fly was near the stone that I felt a pull, but though it seemed a strong enough tug the fish was not hooked. I had seen no rise, so I asked Roderick if he had seen it. " I saw the line go, but no fish showed. Just rest him and maybe he'll come again like the first one—that's if he was no' pricked."

I tried him again but he would not rise any more, so Roderick changed the fly for a smaller one. I asked Roderick if I could put on the fly. " Maybe," he said. " I'm no' wanting to lose the fly, but you'll have to learn sometime."

He showed me the knot. It was more complicated than the one Uncle uses, so I asked if that knot was necessary. He replied " No, but this is the one I've always used, so I'm accustomed to it. It won't draw out, but there are others as good."

Roderick was an old-fashioned person, both to look at and in his ideas. He liked few new things and when I produced a cast of nylon he would not put it on the line. Old ideas are very nice, but so too are some of the new ones, but there was no good saying this to Roderick. He would have none of them.

About the nylon he said, " Och! that stuff! It's just like the skin of an eel. No knots will hold in it and it breaks if you sneeze." But a new pattern fly would interest him. He might not use it, or give it any credit, until he saw someone catch a fish with it. Just at what moment he would decide it was worthy of trial by himself was difficult to say. I doubt if he knew how he made up his own mind, and he certainly could not explain his inner thoughts on it. Experiment for Roderick was something to be avoided and I expect it was largely for this reason that Uncle had said that he was not likely to be a good fisherman on strange waters.

This day was a red letter one for me and I went back with my salmon as happy and as proud as it was possible to be.

" Let's see what the history of this fish is," said Uncle.

" How do you do that?"

" By looking at its scales. All fish keep their history on their scales for us to read. When we get back to the house we'll put some of them under the microscope and see."

Uncle took six scales from the shoulder of the fish and put them on a glass slide. Then he fetched his microscope and examined them.

" Now look! You see all those rings on the scale, rather like the rings in the trunk of a tree that is felled? Well, it's from them we learn its story. The centre ones are fine and small. Those are the parr years and the pre-migratory life. Then the gaps between the rings get wider: that is when he first went to the sea. They get wider because he began to grow fast due to the good food in the sea. The wide spaces continue for some time and then they get narrow again. That narrowing was the first winter in the sea. Even there the food supply is less in the cold months, so the fish cannot grow so fast. That narrowing is called a ' winter band '.

" Then once more the rings get wider apart. That is the sign that the food supply increased and the fish made more rapid growth—the summer period. These scales showed that he spent three years in the sea. Then comes that ragged line where it looks as if the scales had been eaten away: that is a spawning mark. After he had recovered from that, the rings become regular again, showing that the fish went back to the sea and had some more good feeding. Then he came up the river and you caught him.

" This fish then has a life of three parr years, three years in the sea, one spawning mark and some months of sea feeding since, so he was seven and a bit years old."

Chapter XIII

A DAY'S SEA FISHING

IT was a few days after I had caught my first salmon that a friend of Uncle's, Colonel Charlie Macdonald, suggested that all three of us should come with him for a day's sea fishing. This seemed a splendid idea and a date for the expedition was fixed.

" What sort of tackle do we take?" I asked.

" Well, I'm not sure what Charlie has in mind, but there are three possibilities: mackerel, and they're sure to be about at this time of year, lythe, and there are haddock and other white fish. For the mackerel we want silver spinners, for the lythe, rubber eels, and for the white fish, mussels, but Charlie will supply them."

Then he went on to explain that you can fish for all of these fishes with hand-lines, but if you want to get the best fun, a rod is the thing. With a rod it was not likely that as many fish would be caught, but the playing of them made up for any loss in numbers. For the haddock and other white fish, it did not much matter, as the bait had to be let down to the bottom and the angler waited till he had a bite and then hauled the fish up, whether on a hand-line or a rod.

We all went to the gunroom and Uncle produced three old, green-heart spinning rods, short, stiff weapons with big porcelain rings, and three reels, which had on them some coarse line called "Cutty-hunk". These reels were of wood and much bigger than our fly reels.

"Why can't I use my own reel?" asked Ronald.

"Because the salt water spoils a good line in a very short time. If ever you have to use your fly lines in salt water you must wash them in fresh water afterwards. Also the metal of which fly reels are made becomes badly corroded in salt water; that's why they have special reels for sea fishing, like these."

The spinners were just flat pieces of metal, shaped like a little fish with a sort of propeller at the head. In front of the propelling fins there was a swivel to which the trace was fastened. The trace was only a short piece of very stout nylon about 18 inches long and it ended with another swivel to which the line was fastened.

The rubber eels were the queerest looking things. They consisted of a piece of rubber tube fitted over the shank of a great big hook, and looked a little like giant worms on meat hooks. The end of the rubber was loose, leaving the point of the hook and the barb bare. At the eye of the hook there was a big swivel. The rubber tube was tied tight to the shank of the hook just below the eye.

" Do you mean to say a fish will ever take a thing like that?" asked Ronald.

" Oh yes !" said Uncle. " Do you think people would make them if they did not take fish? I have caught salmon on rubber tube baits."

Then there were leads of different sizes. The sea being so much deeper than the river, these baits had to sink down to where the fish are. The leads that Uncle produced were rather like painted sausages, or a baby hammock tied up in a roll. They had a swivel at each end.

" Why do we want all those swivels?" I asked.

" Well, the spinners turn round very fast in the water and if there were no swivels the line would be kinked in no time. The eels also turn and wobble though not so fast as the spinners and the fish when hooked will kink the line if there are no swivels."

" Do we want landing nets?"

" No, Charlie or his boatman will have a boat gaff if it's wanted, but most of the fish we are likely to catch can be lifted into the boat by the trace. These traces are very much stronger than the ones we use in the river and fish of four or five pounds can be lifted without risk," explained Uncle.

We went by car to Colonel Macdonald's home. The house is close to the sea. After leaving the car, we walked to his boathouse where he and his boatman, Allan, were waiting.

It was a lovely day, not much wind and few clouds about. The sea looked calm and a wonderful colour, green near the shore and blue further out.

The Colonel said that we would try for mackerel first as there were plenty about.

"Sir, how do you know where to find them?" I asked.

"Oh! that's fairly easy," he said. "The mackerel feed on herring fry and so do the birds, gulls and terns. Where you see a lot of birds diving into the sea they are after the herring fry and that's where the mackerel will be too."

The bay from which we started is a very sheltered one and there are islands guarding its entrance. Allan headed for a gap between them.

"Now Bob, we'll let these two young fellows start the fishing and we can smoke and give them good advice," said the Colonel.

While we were going out to the islands the tackle was mounted. I think Allan, the boatman, took a poor view of the rods. He preferred hand-lines, but then he was a professional fisherman by trade and his idea was to get as many fish in as short a time as possible, so in his mind a rod was merely a delaying factor.

We were soon round the first island and outside its shelter there was a bit of swell. The launch, which had looked so big at the pier, now seemed smaller and very much less steady. I noticed

Ronald looked rather pale, and I hoped that he was not going to disgrace us by being sick. I whispered to him, " Are you all right?"

" No," he said. " But don't talk to me."

Suddenly Uncle cried, " Look there!" and pointed to a place about half a mile away where there were fifty or sixty birds diving.

" Yes, that looks like them," said the Colonel.

Allan steered the boat towards the place and as we got nearer he slowed down, until we were just crawling.

" Now put out your spinners. Let out about thirty yards of line and hold on."

I took another look at Ronald. He was a better colour. Having something to do seemed to have had a good effect, but I did not ask him how he felt as I feared that talk of any kind might be dangerous.

No sooner had our lines got out to the required length when Ronald's rod seemed to jump and he had a fish on. I was very glad of this, because the excitement of a hooked fish cured his sea sickness far more quickly than any sympathy from Uncle or me.

That fish fought like mad, but I had no time to watch, as my bait was taken before Ronald had landed his mackerel. As soon as Ronald's line was out again he was into another and in no time we had a dozen fish in the boat.

" Now you've had fifteen minutes and it's our

turn," said the Colonel. So we changed places.

"Isn't this fun!" said Ronald, and I knew he was quite well again. I felt nearly as pleased as he did.

The mackerel were taking madly and I think the two grown-ups caught more than we did. Both Ronald and I kept looking at our watches to see if their fifteen minutes were over and just on the stroke Ronald cried, "Time's up!"

They both laughed. "Are they always as punctual as this?" asked the Colonel as he gave up his seat and rod.

Between us we caught 51 mackerel before the shoal disappeared.

"What time is low tide?" asked the Colonel.

"About three," said Allan.

"Well, we'll land on one of the islands for lunch and try for lythe at low tide."

Colonel Macdonald had brought out a marvellous lunch and lots of things to drink. In fact there was too much, and Ronald was doing so well that I wondered if he would be able to hold it all. Uncle, too, seemed to have some doubts about Ronald's capacity, for he said, "Remember, Ronald; lythe are not so plentiful as mackerel. There are long waits between fish and the sea is getting no smoother." Up till now I had not realized that Uncle had seen how uncomfortable Ronald had felt, but there is not much that escapes him.

We went to sea again at about 2.30. We had
some way to go to the place where the lythe were,
and we had time on the way to change the spinners for rubber eels. On one rod we put a red eel
and a grey one on the other.

The Colonel went on to explain that when a
lythe takes, he does so with a bang and as soon as
he feels the hook he rushes for the weed. This
weed is not like the weed in a river or loch, but is
long, tough and very thick. Once a lythe gets in
it he is lost, so as soon as we hook one we must
fight him like mad to keep him out and up. We
could see the weed some way down and the
stalks of some of it were over an inch thick, and
all had very long stems.

We trolled round the rocks very slowly, just
fast enough to make the eels wobble and look as
if they were alive. To get the eels to the right
depth we had put on heavier leads than those we
used for mackerel.

As Uncle had prophesied, the sea was rather
rough and I glanced anxiously at Ronald to see
how he felt. He seemed to be all right and I said
nothing.

At first I concentrated on my line, but as
nothing happened for about ten minutes, I
glanced away and was just pointing out a strange
bird when the rod was nearly jerked out of my
hand. I grabbed at the reel and began to wind in,
mindful of the trailing weed.

Did that fish fight? It felt bigger than a house. "Good," said the Colonel. "Keep him up." Meanwhile, Allan shifted the helm and headed out to sea and away from the weeds. After the first minute the fish rather gave up and I was able to reel him to the boat, but as soon as he saw the boat and Allan with the gaff, he made a most stupendous splashing. However, Allan was used to this and out of a smother of splash he reached out the gaff and pulled the fish into the launch. This fish was dark golden green in colour with enormous eyes, rather like a cod. However I was very pleased. The grey eel was on my line.

At the end of the day we had seven lythe. "How did you like that?" asked Uncle as we drove home.

"It was the best of fun, but I like salmon better," said Ronald. "Still, I would not have missed it for worlds."

Chapter XIV

WE GO TO THE RIVER ALONE AND RONALD HOOKS HIMSELF

SOON after our seafishing trip, Uncle told us to go to the river. "Now Ronald, you have the top beat and John the lower. I'm not going to tell you what flies to put on nor where to fish.

You've both been shown, so let's see what you can do on your own."

" Can we use what tackle we like?"

" Yes, within reason. I don't want all my flies to get lost, so 12 each should be ample, or, if you want to, you can fish with a worm."

" What about one of those funny little imitation fishes all covered with triangles?" asked Ronald.

Uncle laughed. " You mean the phantoms and devons?"

" Yes, if that's what they're called."

" But you do not know how to use them and you want a special rod, reel and line to fish them. No, you'd better stick to the type of fishing you know. One day I'll teach you how to spin, but not yet. Anyway, it's nothing like so much fun as fly fishing."

This was an exciting morning. I tried to remember all the lore I had been told. To be frank, I wanted to do better than Ronald, which I suppose was rather a selfish thought.

When I arrived at the Bridge, the river looked just right and, to encourage me, a salmon jumped as I was putting up the rod. I chose a fly whose name I did not know, but which looked very attractive to me, and started to fish. It was not long before I hooked one. It did not feel very big, but big enough to stop me from pulling it to the surface to see it. My first thought was one of hope that this might be a salmon. Alas! I had not had it on very long when the rod suddenly flew straight and the fish was off. I wound the line up and found the fly gone; obviously the knot had slipped. I could have cried with vexation because I knew it was entirely my own fault. I had botched the knot. I will never know what that fish was, and I felt how gladly I would have made a bargain that if only I could have seen it and known its weight, I would let it go.

A little later I caught a sea trout of about two pounds and with that I had to be content, because I neither caught nor saw another fish.

Ronald had two sea trout and a large eel, which I told him was a poor effort, as he had obviously given up fly fishing for a worm.

" Anyway, worm or no, I've got more than you have," he said.

While we were talking he had left his line in the water and it got the hook stuck on the bottom. He pulled hard and suddenly the hook flew back and hit him a crack on the leg. Such was the force that the hook went in over the barb. " Serves you right for boasting," I said. However, it was well into his leg and it was not easy to see to get it out. I tried, but did not seem to be doing much good, except to hurt him, so we cut the cast, left the hook in, and went home.

We met Uncle in the drive. When we told him about Ronald's hooking himself, he took us back and went in search of scissors, knives, wire cutters, and pliers. Then he cut out a patch of Ronald's trousers, cut off the eye of the hook with wire cutters and said, " Now this will hurt a bit." He then turned the hook round in the leg till the point and the barb came out and pulled the hook through. I must say Ronald was very good about it, as it hurt badly, but once it was out all was well.

I told Uncle about my loss. " It's the way to learn," he said. " You'll lose plenty more fish before you're done, don't worry. If you caught every fish you hooked there'd be no fun in the game. I remember once losing six salmon consecutively. It was my own fault." Then he went on to explain that most people have periods of good and bad luck, but whatever the period is, it is bound to change.

" Oh! Uncle! I saw a big fish jump to-day which looked to me like an enormous, brown trout. What could it have been? I'm sure that no brown trout grow as big as this one was?" asked Ronald.

" That was a reddening salmon," said Uncle. " When he came from the sea he was bright and silvery, but if he has been a long time in fresh water he turns reddish brown. It is his spawning dress, the change takes place as he ripens to spawn. We think it is ugly, but I am sure that the hen fish think he looks very handsome when he's red."

" How big do brown trout grow?" I asked.

" Well, in this river, or in the lochs here, one of six pounds would be a big one, but there are lots of places where they grow very much bigger and there is on record one of 39 lbs., caught in Loch Awe."

" Why don't they grow so big here?" asked Ronald.

" It's all a matter of feeding and to some extent luck. If the food is good and plentiful, and not too many fish to compete for it, and the fish has the luck to survive all the dangers that threaten little fish, he will grow big."

" And are salmon the same?"

" Up to a point, although salmon do not grow big in the river. They go to the sea as smolts when they are about six inches long. You would think that the feeding in the sea would be the same for all, yet some rivers have big salmon and others small ones. We know very little of the life of the salmon in the sea and it is difficult to give reasons for the variation in size of fish in different rivers. But there is no doubt that rivers whose smolts go to the sea young—that is two or three years after they hatch—produce bigger salmon than those which have smolts of 4, 5, 6 or 7 years old. Obviously if the parr remain in the river for more than two years, they eat the food which younger parr would get if they were not there. A river has only a certain amount of food in it and the more little fish there are to eat that food, the less there will be for each fish. To some extent the same laws apply to brown trout: it is no use putting a lot of trout into a loch which has not enough food for them. In fact it will do harm; it is better to put food into it."

"How do you put food into a loch?" I asked.

"You put in the things that will grow there and which the trout like, such as fresh water shrimps and snails, but that isn't all the problem. There must be food for the food, and though we know some of the story, we do not know it all, and, until we do, we are sure to make mistakes."

Chapter XV

WE TRY TO POACH A SALMON

THERE had been fine weather for some days, bright and hot sunshine. The river was very low.

Ronald and I were walking along the bank and looking into each pool to see if we could see any fish. Now there is one pool which has a high, steep bank and the water below it is deep. It is a favourite lie for salmon. We could see into this pool very well by creeping to the top of the steep bank and slowly putting our heads over, and there below was a large, fat salmon. He was plainly visible. For some time we lay watching him. He never moved from his lie.

I do not know which of us had the idea first, but I said, " If we were to get one of those big triangles of Uncle's, we could catch that fish."

" Oh! let's do it," said Ronald.

So off we went to the house without saying anything to anybody. We found a triangle, fastened it direct to the line of one of our rods and went off to the river. We crept up to the bank, peeped over and there was the fish lying just as we had left him.

" Now Ronald, you hold the rod and I will drop the triangle down beside him and jerk it into his side, then you will have to play him till I get back to help."

We were both very intent on what we were doing. I carefully let the hooks down. The fish did not seem to notice them. Then, just as I was going to pull the hooks into him I got such a smack behind. I suppose I had been so busy trying to poach that fish that I had not heard anyone approaching, but Uncle had seen what we were up to and had come down with his gaff and it was the handle of that gaff that hit me. It was the only time I have seen him angry. " You little poachers," he said. " Don't you ever let me find you doing that again. You can catch all you like by fair means but I won't have this poachers' dodge used on my water."

He sent us both home. Later I heard him telling the story to someone else, when he did not know I was there, and he was laughing about it.

" Do you know what I found the little devils doing? They were just about to snatch a fish at the House pool."

" Well, Bob, didn't you try the same dodge at their age?"

" Yes, I suppose I did, and a fish lying like that is rather tempting."

So I knew he was not really angry, but I have never forgotten that gaff handle; indeed I have it to-day.

Later Uncle told us that there were only two occasions when it was right to catch a salmon that way: one was if you were desperately hungry and had to have a fish for food, and the other was, if you saw a diseased fish in the water. It was right to take it out by any means, to save the others from catching the disease.

One day I asked Uncle if there was any chance of catching salmon in very low water.

" Yes," he said, " with very small flies fished near the surface. But in still water there must be a breeze to ruffle the surface, and the line must be greased to keep the fly high up in the water. An ungreased line sinks and drags the fly down with it. When you're fishing a greased line you must give a salmon even more time after the rise than you do with a sunk line, because any movement of the rod or line is transmitted more quickly to the fly with the floating line."

" Won't they take a worm?" asked Ronald.

" Salmon are caught with worms, but generally in heavy water in this country. In Iceland they take a worm very well and nearly all Icelanders use it at any height of water, but I can't tell you why they take worms better in Iceland."

" Can I try a worm?"

" Yes, you may try, but don't expect much with the river as low as it is now."

" Isn't there any bait they'll take when it's like this?"

" Well, some people use shrimps and prawns and they do catch fish, but the prawn is a funny bait. Sometimes salmon take it greedily and at others it seems to frighten every fish in the pool."

" How do you use it?" I asked.

" There are several ways; you can spin it, but I can't see the point of doing this, as a prawn never rotates when it is alive and the motion given to a prawn by spinning is quite unlike anything it does when alive. Then there is what is called ' Sink and Draw '. By this method you drop the prawn in, let it down with the stream, then draw it up in slow, short lifts and keep on repeating this motion over the place where you think the fish are lying. Finally there is an Irish dodge where they use a float. The float is put on the line so as to allow the prawn to drift near the bottom and the angler drops it into the pool and watches the float. When the float bobs below the surface you know a fish is at the bait. Here too you must give him plenty of time, as a salmon often mouths a bait for some time before taking a good hold of it. I have never seen this method used and some river owners do not allow it. Personally, I don't like prawns, but if you use a prawn or shrimp, you must learn how to mount it. Shrimps and prawns in their natural state swim backwards, so when you thread it on to the hook, the point of the hook is at the head of the prawn. Look it up in one of the books and you'll see how it's done."

" Have you got any prawns?" asked Ronald.

" No, I haven't," said Uncle, "and what's more I'm not going to get any. I don't like them."

" If a salmon doesn't eat in the river, why does he take a fly, worm, or any of these other baits?" I asked.

" You may well ask that, and the answer is not easy. Perhaps the best way to make it clear is to say that a salmon has no need of food in fresh water. Occasionally he remembers that, in the past, eating was good fun and the lures we offer him bring to his mind some of the things he used to eat in the sea and, when one passes close to him, he seizes it. Also, you must remember that a fish's mouth is the only means he has of holding anything. To some extent it replaces hands; if he wishes to examine an object, or feel it, he must take it in his mouth."

" Why should baits be spun?" asked Ronald.

" Chiefly to hide the imperfections of the bait maker. No living thing that I know in our rivers, rotates in the water, so it is quite an unnatural movement, but, due to the speed of its rotation, not even a fish can see what the thing really looks like and fish have very good eyes, though they do not see in quite the same way as we do."

" How do you mean, not in the same way?" I asked.

" Well to begin with a fish has monocular vision, that is he can see with both eyes independantly. We, on the other hand, cannot really do this. We use our eyes as a single optical instrument. Then, fish have a range of colours different from ours. They see further into the red than we, but I rather doubt if either of you have done enough physics to understand, so I won't bore you with details. But one useful thing to remember is that the deeper a fish is in the water the more he can see of the land. You can get quite close to a fish in shallow water, but not in deep water, always provided the surface is unruffled by wind or current. In turbulent water he sees little of what goes on ashore."

"Do the trout and sea trout see in the same way?"

" I don't know about all fishes, but all the salmon family do."

" But they do not all behave in the same way,"
I said.

" No they don't. The salmon spends most of
his days in fresh water ripening to spawn; the
trout on the other hand has to eat, so he wanders
around looking for food and ripens at the same
time. A salmon, having no need for food, will
only take something brought to him by the current
and, if it brings nothing, he doesn't mind. Sometimes a trout will do the same, but the stream does
not bring him enough, so he has to go and find it,
especially so in a loch."

Uncle was not always so ready to talk about
fish, but I think he preferred to discuss their habits
rather than ways to catch them. After once
explaining how to catch a fish, he thought that it
was up to us. Now old Roderick was very much
more inclined to talk about catching them, so we
used to ask him all sorts of questions and then try
out the answers.

Sometimes I would ask Uncle the same question that I had asked Roderick. He would reply,
" And what did Roderick say to that?" or, " Ah!
you've been chattering with Roderick."

The natural instinct of all fishermen is to keep
his line taut when he has a fish on and the reasons
for doing this are obvious. But there are occasions
when letting the line go slack is the only way to
save a loss.

One day I was with Uncle at the Nursery Pool

on our river. Here it is impossible to follow a fish downstream beyond a certain point. On this day Uncle hooked a good fish. The river was high and after a time the fish ran down; it got to a point at the tail of the pool below which it could not be followed and a break was certain. The current was a raging torrent after it had passed the tail and there was nowhere for several hundred yards that a fish could rest.

Uncle realized the danger before I did and the moment when the fish hung for a short spell on the lip of the tail he suddenly let the line go slack and pulled off many yards from the reel and let this go too.

" Oh! why did you do that?" I wailed.

" It's the only chance," said Uncle. " He may feel the pull of the line in the current from downstream now and swim up against it."

For some anxious moments we waited, then, sure enough, the fish moved slowly up stream. Uncle did not reel in the slack until the fish was well back in the pool. Then he recovered the line. The fish was still on and we landed it.

" Remember there is a barb on the hook. This should keep the hook engaged and generally it is safe enough. But sometimes if a fish has been on for a long time the hook may have made too big a hole for the barb to do its work and the hook drops out. But, as in this case, the fish would have been lost anyway, so the dodge is worth trying.

" I feel that the remedy is a desperate one but if enough line is let out, the pull on the hook exerted by the current should be sufficient to retain the hold."

Chapter XVI

ON A NEW RIVER AT EASTER

ABOUT three weeks before the Easter holidays started we had a letter from Uncle to say that we had all been asked to stay with a friend of Uncle's and fish his river.

This river is a famous one for Spring fish and very much bigger than the one at home. But the letter went on to say that nice as the invitation undoubtedly was, we were not to build too many hopes about the fishing; it was quite possible and indeed likely that we might fish all the week and catch nothing. On the other hand, there was a good chance that, if the conditions were right, we might do well. So with that we had to be content.

We were so excited at the idea that I, at least, caught a dozen fish every night in bed thinking about the visit.

We went straight from school to this river and were met at the station by Uncle, who had been there for three days before we arrived.

" Have you caught any fish yet?" we both asked.

" Yes, one or two," he said, " but they are not taking well and one or two a day is all we can expect."

" Oh! but that's marvellous," said Ronald.

" Well maybe, but remember there are five rods fishing, though after to-day there will only be the four of us."

We had arrived at 10 a.m. and the arrangements were that we should go to the house, change and then on to the river. Uncle had brought all our tackle and provided waders for us, as these were essential on this river, so we were well equipped.

Our changing was done in record time and in about ten minutes we were ready at the door.

" I suppose you've just flung your things about the room to get ready as quickly as this. Now go up and tidy the place. The housemaid has enough to do without your adding to her work." Rather subdued we went back to our room. I have to admit it was rather untidy, so we cleared up the mess.

The river runs quite close by the house and we could see glimpses of it as we walked down. It looked very big. It was running waist high, swollen with melting snow which still lay deep on the hills.

At the first pool there was a big hut where all

the tackle was kept. It was like a small cottage, had a grand stove already burning brightly, a table, chairs and lockers. Here our host, Captain Roberts, met us and gave us a great welcome. He had been a sailor and commanded his house and river as if they were ships.

As soon as we had greeted him he said, " Now then Bob! You get on to your water; the boys will go together with John. I'm sending them to the middle beat as it is easier fished by youngsters and the wading is better. I'm going down. We'll meet here at 1.30 p.m."

John was the head gillie. He was a man of about 60 with a rugged, weather-beaten face, a droopy moustache and twinkling, blue eyes.

All our gear was ready: the rods up, casts on, but as yet no flies. We put on our waders. They were trousers of full length and felt awkward and stiff. Mine came up to my armpits and Ronald almost disappeared into his.

" Have you no wading sticks? asked John.

" No," we confessed.

" You'll need them. There are some bad stones in the water. I know some young men think they can do without, but you'll be better with one." He went into the hut and produced two hazel sticks, each had a sling on it and a lump of lead on the end. The lead was to make that end sink, so that when you are in the water you can pick up the other end easily.

We had a little way to walk from the hut till we came to a large, long pool. This pool was not like any pool on the river at home, being longer, wider and more like a run than a pool. But John said there were fish in it and that it was deep with many "holes". He took me to the top and told me where to start fishing. Then he asked me about flies. I rather proudly produced my fly box and showed him the flies we used at home.

"Och! They'd be fine in July, but we need something bigger now; the water's cold and the fish lie deep, so we must sink the fly down to them." With that remark he produced an old tobacco tin full of the most enormous flies I've ever seen, more like birds than insects.

He chose one and put it on for me. I should have liked to put it on myself, but I felt rather shy. Elderly gillies often do make young people shy till you get to know them. I noticed he used the same knot as Roderick.

He gave the fly a tug and said, "That'll hold him. Now fish it down slowly and when the fly gets to yon break in the water he may come. After yon break anywhere down the pool. Master Ronald and I will be about 100 yards below and I'll keep an eye on you, so if you get into a fish I'll be right back. The water's full of kelts now, but you'll maybe know one when you see it." And with that he went off with Ronald.

I felt rather pleased that he should think I

could recognize a kelt and, from being rather scared of him, I now felt we were friends.

I looked at my water. It seemed dark, strong and mysterious as if it might hold any kind of a monster. I knew that when the water was as cold as it is now, fish do not jump and show themselves, so I was not expecting to see any.

In one way I was rather glad that John had gone with Ronald as I did not know what he would think of my casting and felt sure that if he had been there I should have botched it. However, all the trees and bushes had been cleared to make casting easy, and the bank was high enough off the water to give me command of the line, so I was not worried.

Ronald told me later that he had wished John had come with me for the same reasons as I had, but he found John so friendly that he soon got over that shy feeling. Whenever he made a bad cast John said, " Never mind, the current will soon straighten it out," and told him what he had done wrong. In fact Ronald's casting noticeably improved after two or three days with John.

I started casting, the huge fly seemed to unbalance the whole line at first, but after a bit I managed the timing of the cast better and I was surprised how easy it was to throw. The wind, fortunately, was helping me. I spent some time above the place where John had told me to expect a fish. I did this to get the feel of the tackle, then

I came down slowly, casting at an angle down-stream and the current did the rest. There was no need to work the fly.

At the top of the pool there was no necessity to wade. Even if I had wanted to, the water was too fast and deep, so I stayed on the bank.

I fished past the break in the water where John had said there might be a fish, but, about five yards lower down, the line stopped in midstream and a slow, strong pull made me tremble all over. I lifted the rod and knew I had hooked something.

I had seen no rise and at first I was not sure that it was a fish, but two or three jerks of the rod confirmed my best hopes. I tried to recover some line, but the fish would not have this, and went off right across the river, taking what seemed to me an awful lot of line. Soon all the line was away and the backing fairly screaming off.

From the corner of my eye I saw John start to come to me and I felt relieved, as I was sure that if this fish did not stop soon he would get away. Afterwards I realized that John could not have done anything if it had gone on, but his presence was very reassuring.

" Have you seen him?" he asked.

" No, but if he goes on like this we never will," I gasped.

" Och! Don't you be worrying; he'll turn."

I do not know how far away that fish got to,

but John was right; he did turn and I was able
to get some line back.

"He feels like a monster," I said.

"Yes, the water's that strong and the weight of
the line you have out will make it feel big.

"I'm no sure he's right," said John rather
glumly, but just then the fish made a sharp run
upstream. As soon as it did this, John said, "Now
I'm thinking it's a fish. Well done you!" I was
rather hazy as to what I had done as yet. It
seemed to me that the fish had done everything
and I had been a post to which it was rather in-
securely tied.

It was some time before we saw anything of it.
All the time it played deep down in the water.
This in some ways was reassuring, as a fish that is
jumping and splashing about on the surface
always seems to me to be insecure. John kept saying, "Put more strain on him," when I felt that
I was already pulling hard enough to tow a boat.

"It's the current," said John. "Ah! there he
is! Yes, it's a fish—take it easy now." From then
on he kept up a sort of quiet, running commentary
on what the fish was doing and what he was going
to do.

In the end we had to go down to a backwater
formed by a recess in the bank. Here John took
the cork off his gaff.

"Now stand you there and bring him to me."
This sounded splendid, but till now there was no

question of my bringing the fish anywhere. It had been the fish taking me about. However, I got the casting line back on the reel and now and again I saw glimpses of the fish in the swirly water looking like fading silver gleams in the shade. I persuaded him into the backwater, at least I suppose I did, because he came there, and in it he swam round and round, never quite close enough for John to use his gaff.

"Don't miss him, John," I said.

John laughed. "Never you mind me, sir," he said. "I'm just biding my time." Later Uncle told me that when there is a gaffer with as much experience as John, you should never try to tell him what to do. The gaffer has his job and it only worries him to be spoken to, especially by an inexperienced and excited angler.

Suddenly I saw John reach out with his gaff, plunge it deep into the water and there, miraculously, was the fish on the end of it. In another moment it was flopping on the grass and John gave it a thwack on the head. Then he removed his cap, scratched his head and said, "My, it's a grand fish! I'm that pleased with you. Ay! and it's weel hookit; just look at that." and he pointed to where the enormous hook was deeply embedded in the corner of the fish's mouth.

"That's just where they should be hookit."

"What do you think it weighs, John?"

"He'll make seventeen, I'm thinking." Actu-

ally it weighed 17½ lbs. Apparently all good
gillies underestimate the weights of fish their
anglers catch. I think it is to please the angler—
which it does—when he finds the real weight to
be a little more.

My arm felt quite numb when the fish was
landed, so I said I would come with him to see
how Ronald was doing.

When we got to him he was wading. He had
seen no fish, but not long after our arrival he
hooked something.

" Now, come out of the water," said John.
" You can't follow a fish unless you are on the
bank, but take it easy, and, whatever you do,
don't fall."

We had not seen the rise, but this fish behaved
very differently to mine. It did not run at all,
just dribbled down the stream. After a minute or
two of this John said, " Just pull him in. He's
nothing but an old kelt."

" How do you know that? You haven't seen
him," I said.

" I know fine by the way he behaves. No ' fish '
would slink and slop like that. You can pull him
as hard as you like. The tackle will stand and we
don't want to be wasting time on him."

Ronald got the fish to the edge, when, to our
horror, John seized the cast and yanked the fish
closer. Then he gripped its tail, took the hook out
of its mouth and flung the kelt back in the river.

Actually the whole operation seemed to take very little time, but even so we did see something of the fish. It was a glittery, hard sort of silver colour and all the wrong shape, more like a fat eel than a salmon. Even if Ronald or I had been alone we would have known it for a kelt. Ronald was disappointed, but he felt that at least he had done something.

"Now sir, there are more fish where that one you caught came from." This was a reminder that it was high time I went back to my water and started fishing again. I began just a little above where I had hooked my fish, but I moved no more. I had fished down to where Ronald had started, when John came up and said we had better go to the hut as it was almost lunch time.

John picked up my fish and we strolled back. The Captain was there and seeing us exclaimed, "Well, how have you done?"

"Oh! sir, I've caught a beauty."

"Splendid! I'm so glad. Yes," as John produced the fish, "it's certainly a fine fish, and you Ronald?"

"I caught a kelt, sir. It was fun, too, but it wasn't hurt and swam away all right," replied Ronald.

"Bad luck! However you've both done better than I have, because I lost a fish—my own fault, I slipped on a stone as I was trying to gaff him and the sudden jerk broke the cast."

" Oh, what a pity," I said. But the Captain
only laughed. " I've done it before and I hope
to do it again many more times." At first I did
not understand this remark, till Uncle explained
that he hoped to live long enough to do it many
more times.

Uncle had caught two kelts.

It was very comfortable in the hut, the stove
warmed it and the lunch was superb. I asked the
Captain to tell me about John and told him how
good he had been with his gaff.

" Yes, John is a good gaffer, perhaps as good as
any man I know. So he ought to be. He's been a
gillie all his life; he's almost become a fish himself."

" Was he in the war?" asked Uncle.

" Yes, in the Seaforth's in the first one and
Home Guard in the second," said the Captain.
" He had a very good first war record, got a
D.C.M. (Distinguished Conduct Medal) and was
wounded three times, but now he lives for salmon.
I suppose he must have seen 10,000 salmon caught
and I think he has forgotten how many he has
caught himself. The wonder to me is that he is
still so intensely interested."

" I thought you had to wait for a salmon to be
on its side before you gaffed it," I said.

" Well most people do unless they are ignorant
or very skilful," said the Captain. " There are
very few men I would allow to gaff a fish deep in

the water for me, but John is one, and a few Norwegians and one or two Canadian Indians I have known."

We talked for a little while after lunch till the Captain said, " We'd better get on to the water. It's not much good after 4.30 at this time of year —too cold."

Ronald and I went back to the same beat, but to a pool lower down. On this pool there is a boat, as it is too big, wide and deep to wade at this height of water. The top of the pool can be waded but even that is not too easy in the spring. However, John sent Ronald to fish the top, and we went to the boat.

" What'll you do if we are afloat and Ronald gets a fish on?" I asked.

" Och, there'll be plenty of time to get back for that."

John rowed out a little way into the stream and then threw out a grapnel which was made fast to a long rope. Once the grapnel had a good hold he sat down and paid out two or three yards of rope at a time. This meant that we were fishing new water every cast or two. Sometimes he would pause as the fly moved over a favourite lie so that I could give it three or four casts. We were about half way down the rope's length when I hooked something. " What do we do now?"

" Pull the boat up and row ashore."

" But if he goes mad and runs down, what then?"

" He won't, very few fish do much when hooked from the boat. Indeed they follow it quite quietly."

This fish did just what John had said it would, and it was not till we were ashore that it came alive. Even then it behaved very quietly and John said, " Yon's a kelt," and he was right. By the time I had it near the bank John had put away the gaff; at the end he hand-lined it just as he had done with Ronald's kelt. It was so well hooked that he had to take a little time and care to remove the fly. Then he showed me the maggots in its gills and they were so numerous that the gills had lost nearly all their colour. When it was put back it swam away quite happily.

" What will that fish do now?" I asked.

" It'll likely take your fly again. I've often seen the same kelt to be caught two or three times in the same day."

" Then the hook doesn't hurt them?"

" Nay in the mouth, but if it's foul hookit, he'll nay come again; they're mair sensitive in their sides than they are in the mouth."

Yet I sometimes wonder about John's theory about their not minding a hook in the mouth. It does not seem a comfortable toy and I remembered my last visit to the dentist.

John had a great respect for kelts and it made him " sair " to see them misused. He spoke with some vehemence about anyone who ill-treated them.

" Do many of them come back after they have been kelts?" I asked.

" No, maybe five in a hundred do. Still it's as weel to give them the chance, because they'll be grand, big fish if they do come."

" What happens to the ones that don't come back?"

" There's no one can tell you that. I expect that they are not active enough when they reach the sea and some seal or porpoise gets them. But a few do come and it is easy to recognize them; they have more spots than a first return fish, almost like a grand sea trout. They're a bit thinner but they put up a great fight if they're hookit."

As the dusk comes on quickly in April we rather hurried over the tail of the pool and then gave it up. Picking up Ronald, we went back to the hut and took off our waders. " Give me them waders," said John, and he proceeded to turn them inside out.

" Why are you doing that?" asked Ronald.

" To dry them. If I left them they would be all damp for you to-morrow."

The Captain and Uncle arrived soon after-wards; neither of them had caught anything. So

we went to the house for tea. I felt rather pleased
that I had been the only person to get a fish, but
I kept quiet about it.

Chapter XVII

A FULL RIVER
AND WE GO SPINNING

THAT evening it rained, snowed, sleeted, and
the wind blew with gale force from the
North-East. By dinner time the temperature was
below freezing point.

" This does not look good for to-morrow," said
the Captain.

" No; looks as if we shall have to spin."

" Have the boys got spinning tackle?"

" No, but they'll be quite happy. I have not
encouraged them to spin, chiefly because I wanted
them to become fly fishers first and to look upon
spinning only as a poor alternative."

" I'm sure that's right. But to-morrow I'll take
one of them with me and you can take the other;
they'll have to learn to spin sometime."

So we went to bed knowing that there was a
new experience for us next day.

The ground was white with fresh snow at
breakfast time and, even from the house, the
river could be seen running bigger than ever.

When we got to the hut John said, " I doubt it's no water for the fly." Spinning rods were mounted. I went with Uncle and John came with us.

Uncle gave me his spinning rod to handle. It was quite light in weight, but felt very stiff. The reel also looked strange; it was one of the multi-pliers. The handle was geared to the drum so that the drum made four turns for one turn of the handle. The line was of nylon, just like a rather thick cast, and there was a hundred yards of it on the reel.

When we got to the river Uncle put about half an ounce of lead between the line and the trace. The trace was about 18 inches long with a double swivel at the top end. As bait he used a Golden Sprat in a scarab. The scarab was merely a sort of celluloid envelope open along the bottom. This was to hold the sprat and to preserve it from the teeth of fish or kelts, and it was fastened together with fine, copper wire. The sprat was armed with two triangles, one half-way down its side, the other at the tail.

All spinning reels have a lever which disengages the ratchet and allows the reel drum to run quite free. The ratchet is disengaged to cast and is only used when a fish is hooked. The normal recovery of the line is done with the drum running free.

Uncle wound up the line until the lead was only about a foot from the tip of the rod, the sprat hanging 18 inches below the lead. Then he swung it sideways and allowed the lead to carry the line out over the river, rather like throwing the hammer. He aimed across and down stream, the lead and the bait made a lovely curve in the air and landed with a plop about 45 yards out from where he stood. Then he waited a moment or two to allow the bait to sink to the right depth and only then began to wind in very slowly. He did not engage the ratchet to wind in. The pull of the current alone made the bait swim and spin and the winding was merely to keep the bait at the proper level and to prevent it from getting hung up on the bottom.

It all looked very simple and I said so. Uncle laughed and said, " Yes it's simple enough, but I don't mind betting that when you try you'll get into the most appalling mess."

He went on casting for some time, slowly moving down the pool. When he was about half-way down, I saw the rod bend. Uncle gave a lift to it and he was into a fish. He put the check on and started to play it. Spinning rods are shorter and stiffer than fly rods, so they do not bend so much. To me, looking on, it seemed as if he was being very gentle with it, but knowing that Uncle is usually very hard on a fish I asked John why he did not put on more pressure. John assured me that there was much more pressure being exerted now than ever there could be with a fly rod. It did not take long before John went down and gaffed a lovely, little Spring fish of about 9 lbs.

Then Uncle said to me, " Here now! Have a cast; you've seen how it's done. Don't touch the reel while casting and don't try to force it out. An easy swing is the one to use. Keep the thumb on the line till you want it to go out, then lift your thumb and let it run. Just before it reaches the water put your thumb back on the line and stop the drum from revolving."

It all sounded very easy. I took the rod. I had thought it looked easy to handle, but the moment I got ready to cast the thing seemed to become possessed of a devil. I swung the bait and did as I thought Uncle had told me, but the bait behaved as if it was possessed: it swung round like a scalded cat and landed in a bush ten yards away. Meanwhile, Uncle and John had thrown themselves on the ground to escape the assault of those flying triangles. Well, we recovered the bait and I tried again. This time it landed in the water about two feet out from where I stood.

" Don't force it; just swing it naturally," said Uncle. I tried again and after a cast or two I got into the way of it and managed to land it somewhere in the river, but never far enough out. So I determined to do better. This time I swung it hard. Out it flew and was going beautifully when all of a sudden it stopped with a jerk in mid-air. I looked down at the reel to see what had stopped it and you never saw such a mess. The whole line looked like a bird's nest, tangled into an appalling muddle.

" Swing the point in till I can catch the line," said Uncle, " otherwise the bait will get caught on the bottom and we may lose it."

John got hold of the line and pulled in the bait. Meanwhile, Uncle took the rod and started to unravel the mess. It took them twenty minutes before it was clear.

" I think you had better learn to cast on the lawn," said Uncle, and he took the rod back when all was clear again and fished on down.

" The water's gettin' thin down there," said John, and at that moment the bait stuck on the bottom and however much Uncle jerked, it remained fast.

" We'll need the otter," said Uncle. John delved in an inner pocket and produced a short, thick stick. It was about 14 inches long, had a bit of lead on one end and a piece of stout cord fastened to each end and making a loose loop. On this was a clip like those used for dog leashes.

John fastened the clip to Uncle's line just beyond the tip of the rod. The stick slid down the line and into the river. The moment it reached the water it sailed out along the line like a toy boat; out and out it went, till it seemed to me to be over 100 yards away. Sometimes it would dive and remain under water for several seconds and then bob up further out.   Meanwhile, Uncle walked quite a long way up stream letting out line as he went, until it seemed to me there must be very little line left on the reel.

" That should do it," said John.

So Uncle stopped and gave several tremendous heaves with the rod. I do not know how the tackle stood it. At first nothing happened, then Uncle let everything go slack and then gave another heave. I really thought something must go this time and it did, the bait was freed. Uncle wound up the line and there was the otter in the hooks of the bait. The idea about letting the line slack was to ensure that the otter got below the bait and exerted its pull from below.

" That's a good otter, John," said Uncle.

" It is that. I seldom lose a bait with it and if it won't shift one then nothing will."

Uncle had often seen this otter before and a number of others like it, but he knew that John liked to have his things praised, so he always said so. I think John knew this, too, but he liked to hear it complimented.

" Can you buy those otters?" I asked.

" Not one like this. I make them myself and there's none like mine in the shops." Meanwhile, he wiped the otter and stowed it in that inner recess in his jacket. I have often wondered what other mysteries that voluminous pocket contained.

The snow started again, so we went back to the

hut. John stoked the stove which soon gave out a glorious heat. I only realized then, how bitterly cold it was outside.

I asked Uncle to tell me some more about the various baits for spinning. He said, " There are nearly as many baits as there are words in the dictionary. No doubt most of them have caught fish. Here, look at this," and he picked up a tackle maker's catalogue from a shelf in the hut. Sure enough there were about a hundred pages of baits and the tackle necessary for their employment.

Uncle went on to explain that he thought that natural baits were the best, but that they were messy things to use and he preferred artificial ones for this reason. He made some himself and the best of his home-made ones were from a piece of rubber tube. This tube can be bought in several sizes. The best sizes for salmon baits were $5/16''$ and $\frac{1}{4}''$ diameter. He uses two colours, one a brick red which is opaque, and a brown which is slightly transparent. These tubes can be bought in any chemist's shop and they can be cut to any length required.

I had seen some spoons in a drawer in the hut and I asked him if he used them. " Spoons," he said, " are a favourite bait in Norway and in Iceland, and much used by the natives of those two countries. I don't like them myself. They are awkward, fluttery things to cast and I think they are bad hookers, but a lot of fish are caught

on them." He told me that some of the tiny ones
can be used with a fly rod and are known as " fly
spoons ".

" Never use a good fly rod for casting a bait or
a heavy spoon. It'll ruin it in no time, and never,
never, fish bait in good fly water. Bait is the
invention of the Devil and has the effect of spoiling good fly fishers and good water. Bait should
only be used when the river is quite unfishable
with a fly."

Just then the Captain and Ronald came in.
They had caught four kelts and no fish. The
Captain had let Ronald play two of the kelts, but
he had not let him try and cast a bait. He
probably knew what would have happened to his
line and reel if he had.

After lunch we tried again for a short while, but
the weather was so cold and unpleasant we soon
gave it up and went home.

The Captain did not use a multiplying reel.
He had what is called a Nottingham reel. This is
just like a fly reel, except that it has a ratchet
release. It is an old-fashioned type of reel and
rather more difficult to cast with and control.

On the way home he said, " You know Bob,
you fellows with these multipliers fish your baits
too fast. I know you'll deny this and I admit for
most of the time *you* don't, but most people do."

" You're right, many people do, but the multi-
plier has some advantages. You can recover in

shallow water more quickly, so you don't get hung up so often and there's no need to fish it fast if you don't want to. What about the fixed spool reels?"

" Abominable things! You wind the handle and nothing happens. Don't you teach the boys to use one."

I liked listening to the two old gentlemen arguing about the merits of their tackle. They had such fixed ideas—though they disliked their spools fixed—and not only the Captain and Uncle were like that, but John and Roderick were the same. They all disliked anything new. Unless an idea or a piece of equipment was fifty years old they thought it was no good. I suppose Ronald and I will be like that some day.

Chapter XVIII

RONALD TRIES TO SPIN
AND SOME OF RODERICK'S WISDOM

ONE day after we had gone home, Ronald said to me, " I'm going to learn this bait casting."

" Grand," I said, " but how?"

" I'm going to borrow one of Uncle's sea rods and reels, take the ratchet out of the reel, which is easy to do, then put a bit of lead on the line and cast on the lawn."

Now Ronald was clever with his hands and tools, as well as being mechanically minded, so what he said about the ratchet seemed to me to be a good idea. I watched him do it and the result was quite good; the reel ran free, rather too free as a matter of fact, because the first cast he made was an over-run that took the two of us ten minutes to unravel.

Uncle watched us from his study window and came out to see what we were doing.

When Ronald told him he said, " That's a good idea of yours, Ronald, but don't lose the ratchet of the reel. As a matter of fact, you will find casting with an absolutely free running spool much more difficult than with a proper spinning reel. Modern spinning reels have a brake on them which is adjustable. This puts a little friction on the drum and prevents the worst kind of over-run. You adjust the amount of brake pressure to suit the amount of lead you have on. However, if you learn to cast with a free reel, your casting troubles are over, because anyone who can cast with one of them, finds the newer ones child's play."

We both tried with the old sea reel and after a little were able to control it to some extent and to throw the lead more or less where we meant it to go.

We asked Uncle if we could try in the river and with a bait. He agreed, not because he liked the idea, but because he thought Ronald's initiative should be rewarded.

As the whole idea had been Ronald's, he was allowed to try first. Strangely enough he hooked a fish, but as there was no ratchet on the reel he forgot to hold the drum when the fish ran out line. The result was an over-run which jammed the whole thing. There he was with a fish on some forty yards away, the reel refusing to give any line or to be wound in. We tried to handline the fish, but that was not a success and in the end it got off. I felt sorry for Ronald as the whole idea had been his.

When we told Uncle of our adventures he, too, was sympathetic, and as a special concession allowed us to take one of his spinning reels. At first we were not very good with it, but, having begun on the free spool, we improved. But we caught no fish.

"Don't become too bait-minded," said Uncle. "Remember what I said about fly fishing. The fly fisher who is good, catches more fish than the bait fisher in a season. There are days when the bait will beat the fly, but they are few. There is another very good reason which applies to people of your income. Baits cost from around 50p to £5 or more. They are frequently lost, and I do not propose to make good the wastage."

This economic fact rather staggered us. Just lately we had neglected the cost of tackle. Relations had been so kind to us we had almost come to think that tackle was free.

"Can't we make our own baits?" I asked.

"Yes you can, but will your baits catch fish?" He promised to teach us to tie our own flies and to make baits, too. "There is a lot of fun to be had from making your own gear. Meanwhile, each of you make a bait out of a bit of wood; bring it to me and I'll tell you what I think of it, but I won't promise to let you put it in the river, as I do not want to frighten all the fish."

I am sure it is nicer to catch fish on tackle that we make ourselves than with bought stuff, and in a fit of enthusiasm I asked Uncle: "Can't we make everything, rods, reels and lines?"

"It can be done with rods and reels. In fact an old friend of mine makes both these articles, but it requires many tools and great skill but even he, clever as he is with his hands, would not attempt to make a line. All these things take a lot of time and you only have short holidays. Better learn to fish first, then later you can try the making of tackle. Anglers in the old days made their lines, but they used horse hair to do it. I've seen these lines but they were coarse and unreliable and could only be cast a short way."

One day I was talking to Roderick and I asked him if he had lost many fish.

" Ay," he said, " I've lost too many, but it's generally my own fault, though not always. There are periods which all fishers go through when they lose fish and in a way it's a gamble. There you are fast in a fish, but just think of how many links connect you to that fish: there's the hook to the fish, cast to the hook, about eight knots in the cast, cast to line, line to backing, backing to reel, reel to rod and then maybe you in the boat and me trying to get it to land. My! it's a miracle that ever any fish is landed!" Looked at in this way, I thought he was right.

" But," I said, " if the tackle is sound, as it ought to be, and the fish is well hooked, you should land him."

" I know," said Roderick, " but there's a big IF in it; you test the knot to your fly and you test a bit of your cast, but I've never seen you test your line, your backing or yourself. Mind, if anything breaks it's your own fault. Lines and backing are just as liable to rot as any other part of the tackle."

" Do you test all yours very often?"

" Not often enough, to my cost, but I do test them now and again. If you'll take my advice you'll do the same."

" Did you ever lose a really big fish, Roderick?"

" I couldna' rightly say, at least half of the fish you lose you never see. Mind, I always think he's big if he gets off, and you'll hear lots of them say they've lost the biggest fish in Scotland. But I'm thinking that little fish get off just as easily as big ones and there aren't so many big fish in the water as there are little ones."

I told him the way that John had gaffed my fish at Easter, because I wanted to hear what he had to say about gaffing.

" Ay, gaffs are just like any other tool. You have to practise with them. An old hand like yon John can do things that the likes of you can't, just because he's been doing it for fifty years and you haven't used one yet. It looks simple and so it is, if you bide your time. Wait till you are sure that you can stick it into him and it's easier for the novice to do this when the fish is lying on his side on the surface. Then, once you're handy with it, you can try the fancy shots, but I've seen many a fish lost at the gaff by people who get excited. They dib and dab and just frighten the fish, the fisher and themselves. Once you make up your mind to have a shot at him, dinna wait. Just put the gaff out and into him and you'll be all right."

" Do you prefer a gaff to a landing net?" I asked.

" For big fish, yes, for trout and grilse, no. You see a fish must have some weight to enable you to stick the point into him; any fish under six pounds hasn't the weight for the gaff to get a fair hold. Nets are fine for wee fish, but for big ones it's kind of awkward to get the fish in. If you have no gaff and only a net, mind you get his head in the net and never lift the net with a big fish, just draw it ashore."

Then he went on to tell me of a tale when he was a young gillie. He was with an old gentleman who hooked a fine, big fish. While they were playing it the head gillie came up. On this river gaffs were not allowed in the Spring, so each gillie had a large landing net. The one Roderick had was a very old one. Well, they got the head of the fish into the net and the head gillie tried to lift the fish. The net was rotten and the fish fell through it. Naturally the fish was badly scared and ran a long way out, taking about 50 yards of backing. Fortunately it was well hooked, but there they were with the fish on and the line running through the hole in the net.

" Wait you," said the head gillie. " I'll cut the old net off and we'll pass the ring of the net over the rod." This was a good idea, but he was a very excitable man. He opened his knife and started cutting, but he cut the backing as well as the net, and it ran out into the river. The fish was now quiet, as during the operations on the net, no pressure had been put on it. Also it was a long way off. So Roderick waded in and picked up the end of the backing and, without disturbing the fish, brought it ashore. They tied it on to the reel end, and the angler was able to wind the knot through the rings and finally they landed that fish. It weighed 35 lbs.

Chapter XIX

SOME LESSONS AND SOME FUN ON THE LOCH

THE first day of the summer holidays, we went to the loch with the boat on it. It was a lovely, July day with a fine fishing breeze and the fish were rising well.

Uncle was with us and we each took turns to row. I was the first at the oars and it was a treat to watch Uncle fishing. I think I enjoy watching a good fisherman almost as much as fishing myself, anyway for a little time. Uncle caught three fish before Ronald had caught one. Then he said, "Now we've something for breakfast. John you have a cast." I took his place in the stern. I could rise the fish and could feel them, and I knew they were taking well, but I could not hook them. Ronald was by this time fairly pulling them in.

"What's wrong with you, John?" asked Uncle.

"I wish I knew," I moaned.

"Have a look at your fly." I did this and found the hook broken at the barb.

"No wonder you can't catch them! How long would you have gone on fishing like that if I hadn't told you?" I remembered then that I had struck the boat with one of my first casts.

" Whenever you hit your fly on something solid, always look at it."

When I started again I was in a hurry, I wanted to catch up with Ronald as he was grinning at my stupidity, and in consequence I started to flick off flies.

" Don't fuss," said Uncle. " You're only losing fish, flies and time." That made two rather bitter lessons learned, but I got three good fish before we stopped for lunch and felt a little better.

At lunch time Uncle asked to see our casts. There were three extra knots in Ronald's and four in mine.

" Wind knots," said Uncle. " Better undo them. They only make weak places in the cast."

" How do they get there?" asked Ronald.

" You put them there in casting, it's faulty timing that does it, though in some winds it's difficult to avoid it. The fly gets blown back, forming a loop, and sometimes it goes through the loop, then when you cast you pull the loop tight, and tighter still if a fish is hooked. As a matter of fact in a well-soaked cast there is not much danger of a break, but in a dry one there is considerable risk."

After lunch the wind dropped and the surface of the loch became glassy, but still we could see good fish rising.

" Now," said Uncle, " this is the time to select

a good rising trout and put a fly in front of him. These trout are cruising, so you have to make up your mind which way one is going and then put your fly so that he can see it. If he does see it, he's almost sure to take it. I think that this form of fishing is the very best of fun."

We tried, but neither Ronald nor I could forecast the route the trout took. But Uncle did at once. As a matter of fact, when he did this, I saw him smile and I wonder if he was not rather lucky. Anyway he was pleased, as well he might be, with a trout of $2\frac{1}{4}$ lbs.

" I believe we could use a dry fly on these fish," said Uncle.

We rowed to the nearest shore and there he greased his line to make it float, then he produced a fly which had a long, stiff hackle and wings that stood upright; this he oiled to make it float. The oil prevents the feather fibres from getting water-logged.

When all was ready we went out in the boat again, but Uncle would not allow us to row as he said the oars disturbed the water too much, so we gave the boat a tremendous push out from the shore and glided to the fish.

A fish rose near the boat and Uncle made several false casts to obtain the right length of line and then shot the fly out to where he thought the fish could see it. The line and fly both floated, so we could see everything that happened. It was

some time before he found a fish that was willing
to take it. He missed several and excused himself
by saying, " I'm no expert with the dry fly, but
men who are would not have missed those fish."

" Do you ever use a dry fly in the river?" I
asked.

" Sometimes, especially for sea trout. Salmon
do not often take it, but I have caught salmon on
a floating fly in Iceland, but only when there
were great numbers of natural fly on the
water."

He explained that in the river it was essential
to fish the dry fly upstream to prevent " Drag ",
by which he meant the fly being given a false
motion by the drag of the stream on the line or
cast. No natural fly, and that is what it is supposed
to represent, gets dragged about like an artificial
fly on the end of a cast, which is bound to happen
if it is fished downstream.

The fly has to sit on the water as if it was un-
attached. Then you wait and hope the fish will
come and take it.

" If you want to learn about dry fly fishing, go
and read some of the books about it. There are
several in the library."

" Which is the best?" asked Ronald.

" That's a difficult question to answer, but the
best manual is probably the Lonsdale Library
volume on Trout Fishing. Anyway, all of them
are better reading than the tackle makers' cata-

logue. That at present seems to be your favourite book."

" But there are so many exciting things in the catalogues and letters from people saying how many and how big are the fish they've caught."

Uncle laughed. " Those catalogues are only interesting reading when you haven't the money to buy what they advertise. After you have some money they are just a list of commodities; a good dictionary is far more fun to read."

" A dictionary. Oh! how dull."

" My boy, a good dictionary is fascinating reading, and can tell you more about most subjects than you are ever likely to know. You try it sometime, but take a big one, not one of the so-called pocket ones."

That night I took out Uncle's big dictionary and I found he was right; there's an awful lot in it. The only trouble is where to start and when to stop.

" What is the best book about salmon fishing?" asked Ronald.

" That depends who's reading it. To my mind the best account of catching and losing a salmon is in *Sport* by Bromley-Davenport. There's only one long chapter about salmon fishing in the book, but I think it is the best account of the game ever written. Then there's *Letters to a Salmon Fisher's Sons* by Chayter. You should read them both."

Chapter XX

A VISITOR JOINS US

A DAY or two later Uncle said, " Your cousin Joan is coming for a week or ten days. She's a keen angler, so you must look after her."

" Can she fish?" I asked.

" Yes, she's rather good."

" Oh, we mustn't let her beat us," said Ronald.

" Now Ronald, that's not the right way to think about a guest or about fishing. Fishing is not a game like cricket or football and it does not matter who gets fish or fishes; numbers are not important and one good fish, no matter who catches it, is better than ten little ones. What matters is that when you have a guest they should have a good time. So don't let me hear of competitive ideas creeping into your fishing."

" I didn't mean it quite that way," said Ronald.

" No, I don't think you did, but I just wanted to emphasize the importance of not letting numbers and your own catch obsess your mind."

Joan arrived a few days later. She is a year older than I am. We were rather shy of her at first and I think she felt the same. We were glad to see that she had brought her own rod with her and that we did not have to equip her with tackle;

not that I grudged her any, but my stock was getting low and my supply of pocket money lower.

That morning we took her down to the river, and it was not long before we realized that she was just as good an angler as we were; in fact I think she was rather a better caster.

Uncle came and joined us while we were putting the rods up.

" Now, where are you suggesting that Joan should start?" he asked, although I know that he had made up his own mind on that subject.

" Well," said Ronald, " she must catch a fish, so I think she should start at the Bridge Pool."

" That's a good idea," said Uncle. " Yes, she'll have as good a chance there as anywhere."

Then Uncle left us and we went on to the Bridge. Joan had been on the river before, but she turned to Ronald and said, " What fly should I put on?" As a matter of fact I think she knew better than Ronald what fly to put on, but her asking pleased him very much, which all goes to show that Joan was a shrewd young lady. Ronald chose a fly for her and went on to tell her where the fish lay and how to fish the pool. In fact, from the moment of her asking about the fly, Ronald was devoted to her.

I left them and went on down the river. When I got back they had four sea trout, of which Joan had caught three.

She came with us that evening after dinner, but

it was getting a bit late in the season for night
fishing and I was the only lucky one, catching a
fish of 3½ lbs. Once the middle of August is past,
night fishing has to finish earlier, as the nights get
much darker and it is seldom worth while fishing
after 11 p.m. Summer Time. I asked Uncle about
this, and his verdict was that night fishing was
over, and the second half of August was dusk
fishing. " Remember we use Summer Time and
the fish don't."

I thought that it might be a good idea to try in
the very early morning, so I arranged with Joan
and Ronald that whichever of us woke up early
should rouse the others. The idea may have been
a good one, but the West Highland air made us so
sleepy that it was three mornings later before any
of us did wake up in time, there being no alarm
clock in the house.

We hastily put on some clothes, did not wash
and were on the river at 5 o'clock. Ronald caught
a small sea trout, but neither Joan nor I caught
anything. I felt rather disappointed, so later in
the day I asked Roderick why we failed. He said
we were too late, but if the river had been in
order—it was low at the time—we might easily
catch a salmon between 5 and 7. But on the whole
it was hardly worth the effort, except that to be
out at that time of day was lovely. Everything
seemed so fresh and new and we seemed to have
the whole world to ourselves. It was quiet, clean

and the birds just greeting the new day. For this feeling alone it was worth while.

I have gone out in the early morning many times since and always found it wonderful, but to be honest, I have never caught more fish then than at any other time of day.

Joan was quite good in a boat, but preferred fishing from the bank. I think she felt that the boat was a kind of prison and after a short time in it she wanted more freedom of movement than it allowed. She always fished her water very quickly—a good habit, provided you are prepared to fish it a second time, but with Joan there was no second time down for her. I think she misses a lot of fish by being impatient.

One day I said to her, " Joan, there's plenty of fish here. Give them another chance."

" No," she said. " I've offered them the fly once and that should be enough."

" But surely when you are fishing you are really saying to the fish, ' Please, please, take my nice fly,' and if you rather rudely say to them, ' Here's the thing for you; take it or leave it,' they will undoubtedly leave it." But it was no good. She went on in her own sweet way; but she enjoyed it, which is what matters.

I asked Roderick what he thought about her fishing. He pondered for a while before replying and then said, " Ay, she's no' a bad fisher, but she bangs her fly on the water and takes it out again before most of the fish can make up their minds what to do about it."

Uncle said, " She'll grow out of the habit. I'd sooner she was like she is, than become a slow fisher. Slow fishers don't catch more fish than fast ones, and they merely irritate the man who has to follow them."

No drift in a boat was fast enough for Joan. To have pleased her a speed boat was what was needed. But with all her fiery enthusiasm she was not slipshod; all her knots were well tied, and all her tackle was well cared for. She would discard a worn cast as soon as it showed a defect, and she caught fish. She was as happy on the burn as on the river, the sea or the lochs. We were all very sorry when she left.

Chapter XXI

REPAIRS AND RODERICK TALKS
ABOUT FISHERMEN

" HAVE you got any pocket money left?" asked Ronald one morning.

" A little," I said.

" Then, can you lend me some? I must buy some flies and I can't go on asking Uncle for them. He's given me so many."

" I don't know that I have enough to buy many, but here's £1.50."

" Thanks awfully, I don't know when I can pay you back."

" You've been flicking off so many flies lately, you'll soon flick off £1.50's worth," I said.

" I know and I don't seem able to cure myself." At that moment Uncle came in. " Cure yourself of what?" he asked.

" Flicking off flies."

" Get your timing right. It's probably only that. You start your forward movement too soon, like cracking a whip behind your back; I sometimes do the same myself, especially in a wind."

Uncle picked up my reel. " When did you last oil it?" he asked. I had not thought of that and he was quite right in thinking it needed oil. After I had oiled it, the reel ran as if it was new.

Another dodge he told us was to look at our top rings every now and again. These are made of agate and sometimes they get cracked. Nothing ruins a line more quickly than a cracked agate ring. It cuts the line like sharp glass.

Uncle would dole out these tips from time to time, but only a few on any one occasion, because he thought we were more likely to remember them in small doses.

Once, when we were by the river, he said to me, " Now I'm a complete novice, I've never fished before. Tell me how to start, how to cast, where to fish and what I'm doing wrong."

This was rather fun and he would deliberately make mistakes and go on making them till I told him to stop. I now believe we learnt as much from this form of teaching as we did from all the others.

" When I'm not there, imagine you yourself are the pupil and the master as well and give yourself the lesson," was a favourite theory of Uncle's.

" But," he said, " never tell another fisherman what to do unless he asks you, in case he thinks you are showing off."

We had a guest one day who was not a very clever caster and I wanted desperately to show him how it ought to be done, or, to get Roderick, who was with us, to show him. He was not fishing the water and missed lots of chances. But Roderick. said, " No, he would not be verra pleased." So we kept quiet.

After a time Roderick whispered to me, " It's gey hard to watch someone making a mess of the pool and you not able to say anything, but you just have to sit and twist your toes, and mind it's only your toes, because he canna see inside your waders." It was then that I realized that Roderick was a good judge of men.

" There's funny habits about fishing," said Roderick a little later. " Now take the gaffing of a fish; if your Uncle sends me out with a gentleman and he hooks a fish, then I gaff it and there's nae question about the matter. But if the same gentleman is not out with me and I happen along while he's in a fish, I must ask him if he would like me to gaff it. He'll probably be glad I've turned up, but I've known many who would decline the offer. Yet these gentlemen would never mind if I had been sent out with them at the start."

" But surely that's rather silly?"

" Maybe it is, but that's the way of it. Never offer to gaff a fish unless you're a professional gillie. Wait till you're asked. Mind, it's a nasty feeling if you make a mess of the job and the fish is lost. When I was younger I've done it and the fault was all mine and there's some natures that are no' forgiving after such an accident."

" What did they say?" I asked, full of curiosity.

" Weel, some said one thing and some another and none of them verra polite. But it's understandable; if a man has come a long way for his only holiday in the year and the only fish he hooks is lost because you're inefficient, you canna blame him if he says something to relieve his feelings. Anyway, they laugh about it the next year."

" Does Uncle say things to you?"

" Nay, he just says nothing, but the look he gives is worse. Now the Admiral, him who comes in June, he's a fine gentleman, but he's sairved so long on ships he's acquired a special language for disasters. Forby there are times I'm tempted to lose a fish for him, just to hear what he'll say."

" But Roderick, you'd never do that really?"

" Well, no; I don't suppose I would," said Roderick, rather as if he were contemplating such an action. " But man, he's got a grand vocabulary."

Just then Ronald turned up. He was in despair. He had lost a good fish and broken his rod at the same time. He told us how he was just trying to get the fish into the net, holding the line tight and had the rod bent to near the breaking point, when the fish gave a strong kick with its tail and the top joint broke and so did the cast.

" Bad luck," I said.

" I've done the same myself," said Roderick. " But never mind! I'll mend it for you and it'll be just as strong as before."

" Oh! can you, Roderick?"

" Och! that's easy, come away to the house and I'll have it fixed for you in an hour."

So off we went to Roderick's cottage, where he produced some strong silk and made a beautiful binding of the top joint, finishing it so neatly, that it might have been done in a shop. Then he gave the binding a coat of quick-drying varnish and told Ronald that it would be fit to fish with in an hour. But he advised Ronald to use the spare top for a day, to allow him to give the mended one another coat of varnish; this would let the splice set harder.

Ever since that day I have kept a length of

binding silk ready waxed in my cast case, so that such a repair can be made by the river bank and enable me to go on fishing instead of losing half a day.

Ronald was lucky that the break did not occur just at the ferrule. A break there is generally clean across the grain of the wood and no binding will ever repair that kind of accident. If that happens, you have to take the stump of wood out of the ferrule and refit it. This is not always an easy task and requires more tools than fishermen carry about with them. It also shortens the rod by the amount of wood taken out of the ferrule, but does not as a rule spoil its fishing qualities.

Care has to be used in taking the old stump out of the ferrule because it is easy to " bell mouth " the thin brass. If this occurs the ferrule is useless and a new one has to be found.

I said to Uncle, " It's very handy having some-one like Roderick to do repairs." He nearly burst with indignation.

" Do you think I can't repair a rod as well as Roderick? In fact I taught him all he knows about it and the sooner you learn the better."

Chapter XXII

A TALE ABOUT ICELAND
WE PLAN TO GO THERE

" HOW would you like to go to Iceland next summer?"

There was no need for Uncle to have asked the question, as he already must have known the answer. We both said that there was nothing that we would like better.

" Well," he said, " I've taken a river there for a month next summer and we'll all go."

" Oh, that's just grand," said Ronald, and then went on rather forlornly, " but it's ages we'll have to wait, why it's nearly seven months." Seven months at Ronald's age seems like a lifetime.

" Let's get the map out and see where it is," I said. An atlas was found, but the scale of the map of Iceland in it was so small that it was difficult to make out any details of the country, let alone the river.

" I think I have some maps put away somewhere. I'll look for them; they should be in this drawer. Yes, here they are," and Uncle spread out some sheets of maps on the table.

" This is where we're going—a north coast

river. It should be good and I have fished it before. Also I know the farmers there."

"Tell us about it," I said.

"Well, it's not a big river—about the size of ours here. It depends for water on the winter's snow, so I hope that they have a good fall. The late summer on the north coast of Iceland is apt to be dry."

"But I thought that Iceland was where all the depressions came from," I exclaimed.

"So the meteorologists tell us. But they are generally wrong. I suppose they choose Iceland as a convenient source, because they thought that few people would ever go there and find them out. After all, they have to find *some* place where their depressions start."

I do not think Uncle has a very high opinion of meteorologists.

"But they can't always be wrong," said Ronald.

"No, perhaps not. But their chief trouble is that they are so busy reading their instruments they seldom have time to look out of the window."

During the rest of the winter holidays we read what we could find about Iceland. I think Uncle must have got rather tired of our questions and wished he had not told us till later that he had arranged this trip.

I put the forthcoming visit into a special sort of niche in my mind and only brought it out occasionally and when I was alone. The time passed quicker than I had imagined; we had so many other interesting things to do.

One day, about three weeks before the end of the summer term, Ronald said to me, " You know this Icelandic trip is nearly on us. What are you doing about tackle? I've not been able to save much lately and we shall want masses of things."

" Don't worry about that. Uncle told me that he was seeing to all we needed and I know that he would not let the trip be spoilt for want of a few extras."

We were to meet Uncle on the 23rd of July. The ship sailed from Leith. Until we were in the train we had hardly realized that at last the great adventure had started. The train was very full and rather uncomfortable, but we did not mind that. At Edinburgh we were met by Uncle.

" We've got to sort out your baggage and send the things you won't want home and re-pack those you do want. As we have to be aboard by 6 p.m. there's plenty to do."

In the hotel there were numerous packages of tackle, waders and clothes. It seemed we would never be able to get it all in, but after an hour or so, most of it was packed. Bundles of unwanted clothes were put in a trunk and the hall-porter promised to see they were sent home.

There were one or two things still to buy and

we got them that morning. " Now both of you have to have your hair cut. You won't be able to get it done on the farm, so see that the barber cuts it short."

" Why don't we fly there?" asked Ronald.

" It's very much more expensive with this amount of luggage," said Uncle. " I admit it's quicker, but I prefer one foot on the ground and I like the sea voyage."

" I think the voyage on the ship will be great fun," I said.

At tea time Ronald and I were suffering from travel fever, but Uncle was quite calm.

" Hadn't we better start?" Ronald asked.

" Why?" asked Uncle. " There won't be any customs officers there yet and I prefer this chair to a wind-swept dockside. We won't be able to get on board till the Customs men arrive."

At 5.30 we drove to the dock. The formalities were trivial and in ten minutes we were aboard looking for our cabins. Ronald and I shared one and Uncle had one to himself. Dinner was at seven and we sailed at nine.

It was a lovely evening and the Firth of Forth was as calm as the loch at home. We dropped the pilot at North Berwick and then Ronald and I went to bed. We were rather sleepy after the journey from London.

We woke early and Ronald looked out of the

scuttle and said, " I wonder where we are?" I turned him away from the scuttle and had a look myself. There was a rather flat looking coast occasionally dotted with small, white cottages, they looked grand in the early sunlight. We dressed hurriedly and went on deck. There were not many people about and we felt rather shy about asking strangers. Ronald suggested waking Uncle.

" I shouldn't if I were you. He's apt to be a bit grumpy if he's wakened too early." However, it was not long before he too was on deck.

" Can't sleep the first night at sea," he grumbled.

" Where are we?" we both asked.

" That's the coast of Sutherland. We're making good time in this fine weather." The breakfast gong sounded, so we went down to the dining saloon.

Uncle knew several of the other passengers. Some of them were Icelanders and there were a few Englishmen going to fish. They talked about the rivers and hoped to hear how the fishing was in Iceland.

We were turning West into the Pentland Firth by noon and could see the Orkneys. Here the sea became rougher and I thought Ronald was look- ing rather green. However he came to lunch, but his usual enthusiasm for any meal was absent. After lunch he went to our cabin where I thought it was best to leave him. When I went on deck Uncle asked, " Where's Ronald?"

" Lying down. I don't think he's feeling too grand," I said.

I asked him if all the birds following the ship would come with us to Iceland, as some of them seemed to have come all the way from North Berwick.

" Oh! no they haven't. They keep changing, but you don't notice them do it. Besides, most of these are gulls and they only come a short way from land. Soon they will all be gone. Their place will be taken by Fulmars. The Fulmar is not a gull, though to the uninitiated he is often mistaken for one. He is a petrel and a true ocean bird. Going north at this time we won't see any migratory birds, but on the way back we will. The last time I came back five Grey Wagtails came all the way with us."

" Look at the porpoises," I cried. There was a huge school all going west.

" Seems to be a lot of them," said Uncle. " Why there must be hundreds there! I don't ever remember seeing so many."

A man standing beside us said, " It's almost like a migration, but I never heard of porpoises migrating before. But whales do."

" Yes," said Uncle. " I travelled with an old Norwegian whaling captain on this route a few years ago. He had been thirty years in the Antarctic on the whaling ships and what he didn't know about whales didn't seem worth bothering about. He would show me whales and tell me by their spouts what kind they were. He came to stay with me for a week as he was a keen fisherman, but he thought no fish under twenty tons in weight should be allowed any latitude, and a salmon as soon as hooked, should be pulled ashore like a flounder. He did not catch many, but he was a great character and some of his polar tales were fun to listen to."

The voyage passed almost too quickly and I thoroughly enjoyed it; so, too, did Ronald, after the first day.

We arrived at Reykjavik at 8 a.m. on the Thursday. There we were met by a friend of Uncle's; he was the man who had made all the arrangements for taking the river. His name was Kristian. As soon as we were through the Customs, Kristian took us to our hotel. We were to spend that day in Reykjavik and go north to our river by car the next morning.

Reykjavik is a funny, little town. It is rather nice and very clean, except where it is still being built; there it is incredibly untidy. I asked how they managed to keep it so clean.

" Well you see we have no smoke," said Kristian. " We do all our heating, cooking and washing by water brought in pipes from the hot springs. We do not burn any coal, all our electricity is generated by water power, and we have no railways, so there is no smoke to dirty the place."

Looking round there seemed to be something missing. For a time I was puzzled, and then I realized that there were no trees. Kristian explained that Iceland was beyond the Northern limit of trees, but in some places they were now trying to grow them.

He pointed out the city's garden and said, " Here you see a few trees."

" Trees!" said Ronald. " Those are rowan bushes, not trees." And I must say they were only about five feet high. However Kristian seemed to think a lot of them, so I nudged Ronald, because I did not want him to say anything that might offend Kristian.

We saw most of the town, and in the harbour were a great many fishing boats, all of which seemed to be very busy. Uncle explained that sea fishing is the most important industry in Iceland. On it the Icelanders depend for all the things they have to import, so a good fishing season means prosperity and a bad one means that they have to do without many of the things they need.

We soon went to bed because we had to make an early start. It was a long drive to our river. The car came at 8.30 and we left soon after. The drive took us along the coast and we crossed a number of rivers on the way. They all seemed small, but we were told that some of them were good for salmon.

There is a long fiord called Hvalfiord round which we had to go. This fiord has a whaling station at its head. We stopped here to see it. There was a whale on the slip ready to be cut up.

I have never been to such a messy, smelly place before. The stink reached us some time before we arrived and, on the slipway, the slime was ankle deep. But it was interesting to see. The men were at work on the carcase armed with long handled knives, like short scythes, only the cutting edge of the blade was on the outside. They cut up the whale surprisingly quickly.

" Now whatever you do, don't fall down in that slime," said Uncle. " If you do, you'll stink till we get back to Scotland." I am sure he was right.

Soon after this we came to the first big river we had seen, the Hvità. It is a glacier river and the water in it is just like watered milk. We were told that a great number of salmon run up this and several of its clear water tributaries are among the best fishing rivers in Iceland. The Hvità is the biggest river I have yet seen anywhere.

Uncle explained to us that salmon cannot spawn in glacier rivers, because the ova gets smothered in the silt. So no salmon runs up a glacier river unless it has clear water tributaries.

Just where the clear water comes into the milky water is a very good taking place. At first the clear water does not mix and for a short distance a distinct line between the two waters is visible; the salmon pop out of the opaque water to take a fly in the clear. I think this fishing must be rather fun.

After we left the Hvitá we came to a lava field. Never before had I seen such a muddle of rocks. It looked as if some giant had scattered thousands of tons of coke about and just left it lying for some-one else to sweep up. We lunched in the lava field and then went on to climb the divide which separates Northern from Southern Iceland.

As we went the farms got fewer and fewer till they finally disappeared and we were driving through a bleak and desolate countryside of bog, moss, and rocks. There were still drifts of last winter's snow by the roadside.

" What are those posts for?" asked Ronald.

" That's to show travellers where the road is in winter when the snow's deep," said Uncle.

It seemed a long climb to cross the divide, but at last we were at the top and could look down to the sea on the north coast.

" You see that fiord? That is the one into which our river flows." From where we were it looked tiny, but as we came down it grew bigger.

We got to the farm we were to stay at, at 4 p.m. The farmer and his wife met us and gave us a great welcome. A huge tea was then made for us with pancakes and cream and many other cakes and buns.

" You won't always get a tea like this," said Uncle. " This is just by way of greeting."

We were very comfortable in the farm; Ronald and I shared a room and Uncle had one to himself. We had a sit-dining room, but the washing and other arrangements were a bit primitive.

Chapter XXIII

ICELAND

THE river ran past the house and was only about three hundred yards away. Both Ronald and I were anxious to go to it at once, but Uncle said, " Now, have a little patience! Get your gear unpacked, stowed and arranged so that you can find things. These fish have waited at least three weeks for us, so another half hour won't make much difference to them." This was of course just common-sense, but sometimes common-sense is rather irritating.

Uncle went on to explain that the fish here were fairly big by Icelandic standards and they were just fresh from the sea and very worthy opponents, so we should make sure that we had all our gear in order.

After these chores were done, he said, " Now put on your waders. You'll need them." This took no long time and a few moments later we were on our way to the river.

When we got to it the first thing I noticed was how incredibly clear the water was. You could see every stone on the bottom in a depth of many feet. I had thought that our river at home was clear, but it was like thick soup compared with this water. Another fact that became apparent at once, was that it was very cold—colder even than our river in March. This was due to most of it coming from the snow fields. In size it was a little bigger than our home river and there was a good deal more water in it at this time, but Uncle said it was on the big side now and, unless there was rain, it would drop at least a foot.

" Now that you are here I want you to realize there are lots of strange, new things to see besides fish, so use your eyes. Study all that you can and make the holiday a broadminded one. Don't go back home and only be able to tell your friends that you caught 50 fish." Uncle then laughed, " After that lecture, let's catch one."

" Do you think I really will catch 50 fish, Uncle?" asked Ronald.

" Quite easily, but I was giving you a lecture for the good of your soul, not for the entries in your game book," laughed Uncle.

The river at this point had cut itself a deep

gorge in the bottom of which it now ran and just below where we were standing was the House Pool. It looked splendid, a nice, fast, rough water head, and a swirly middle running out into a long, glassy tail.

" Now this pool is not one of the best. It holds fish in some seasons, but it is a high water pool. There is insufficient depth to hold them in low water. Still it's worth trying, but don't be disappointed if there is nothing there. Ronald, you shall start."

Ronald fished it down but we saw nothing. "All right, let's leave this and go on up. You see those high rocks about 300 yards off? Well, that's Green Box and it is one of the best pools in the river."

To reach it we had to cross a fair-sized tributary which came into the main river at the tail of Green Box. At its lower end, the pool is deep and still, with high rocks on one side and a cliff on the other. Uncle explained that here we had to fish upstream and if we hooked a fish we could not follow it. If he went up, we just had to hang on and hope that there was enough line on the reel. At that moment a fish rose on his own.

" That's a good sign," said Uncle. " We'll get into one here."

Ronald started and made a few preliminary casts to get the right length of line and then cast just where the fish had risen. That fish rose at once, a big, boiling rise.

Fishing upstream makes the hooking easier. When the line is tightened, it draws the hook back into the fish's mouth rather than drawing it away.

" I think you're into a big one," said Uncle, and so he was. No sooner had the fish felt the pull of the line when he rushed straight upstream; eighty yards he went and then jumped. Even at that distance we could see he was a grand fish.

" Oh! what shall I do? He'll have all the line and I can't follow."

" Don't worry, he'll come back, he's about as far as he can get," consoled Uncle. Well, that fish turned and came down like a torpedo. Ronald was winding as if his life depended on it, but even so there were yards and yards of slack line. I think that the fish was going so fast that its speed kept the fly taut in its mouth.

" I've seen many a fish get off by that trick," said Uncle—a remark that did nothing to cheer up Ronald. However, he was too busy to pay much attention. I do not know how long it was before he managed to get a tight line on that fish, but it seemed to me ages, and to Ronald it must have seemed longer. Three times he made rushes up the stream and each time he jumped. It was at least twenty minutes before he showed signs of tiring, but at last Ronald brought him to a place where Uncle was able to gaff him.

He was a lovely fish. " Oh! what do you think he weighs?" asked Ronald.

" Well, he's twenty at least," I said.

" Yes, and more," said Uncle. Actually, he was
$22\frac{1}{2}$ lbs. and the biggest fish Ronald had so far
caught.

" Now John, it's your turn," said Uncle.
" There are lots more fish in the pool." We had
been some time admiring Ronald's fish, so the
pool was rested. These fish were all fresh from
the sea and ready takers. Also they had not been
fished over before, so were unaccustomed to
anglers' flies.

Just the same adventure happened to me—a
few casts to get the line and then I was into one.
Mine was not as big as Ronald's, but he behaved
in much the same fashion. After about fifteen
minutes Uncle was able to gaff my fish, which
weighed fifteen pounds.

" Now, we'll leave these fish here in this little
cave. In Iceland you have to hide all your fish,
otherwise the ravens get them. After the skuas,
ravens are the greediest birds I know."

We went on up the river. We had about 400
yards to go, over some very rugged country, with
huge stones like cottages piled up anyhow. " I
should have liked to see these stones all hurled
here," I said.

" Yes, if they all came at the same time, but
these piles look to me as if they had been built up
gradually over many centuries," said Uncle.

" Aren't they all volcanic?" I asked.

" No, I don't think so, but I'm not a geologist. However, I think most of the rocks here were glacier borne and just left lying when the ice went, and that took a long time."

The next pool was called Foss Run, as it is a long, deep run below the Foss Pool. " Uncle, you must fish this," said Ronald.

" All right, I'll have a try," he said.

" It looks very shallow," I said.

" There's more water there than you'd think. If you tried to cross you'd have to swim."

Uncle caught a fish of 12 lbs. in it. " Now each of us have a fish. We had better go home, because Gunnar's wife will have supper soon. It would never do to be late for the first meal, especially as I know she will have produced delicacies for it."

So we carried back the fish and put them out to be admired on the grass by the front door. They did look nice. They were so bright and fresh. Gunnar came and looked, then pointing to Ronald's fish said " *Store lax,*" which Uncle said means " Big salmon " but Gunnar did not think the other two were worth any mention.

We went to bed in broad daylight, which I found rather strange, but Ronald was so sleepy he did not seem to notice.

Next day we were up early, but breakfast was not ready till nine. " Don't worry," said Uncle. " We've all day ahead of us and the fish can't run away. The back door is locked."

" Why do you say the back door is locked?" I asked.

" Well, they can't get beyond the Foss and from the Foss to the sea the river's all ours," said Uncle.

When the breakfast did come, it was very good and even Ronald, who does himself well at most meals, was satisfied. Packages of sandwiches were ready for us and we went down the river.

On the rivers at home there is nearly always a path along the bank and bridges over the tributary burns, but in Iceland there is nothing like that. The river banks are just as they were before the first Icelander ever got there. This makes the walking harder, especially in waders; the banks are very steep and many of them over a hundred feet high, but it is rather a nice feeling, almost as if one was an explorer in a strange, new country.

There are about two miles of water on the middle beat and ten pools in it.

In this part of the river the pools are not long, but round and deep and in many of them you can stand or sit on the bank and see the fish in the pool below. This was rather exciting. Uncle had a pair of polarizing glasses, which make it easy to see into the water. I think he was sorry he had told us about the polarizers, because we were always asking for them. He feared that we might break them, and he had only the one pair.

These polarizers help enormously. They remove the glare from the surface and sometimes it's almost like lifting a cloth off the water when you put them on.

"This seems to be the country in which to learn about salmon," I said. "They're so easily seen."

"Yes," said Uncle, "while they are in the rivers you can learn more about them here than almost any other place in the world."

That day we caught five salmon. We should have had more, but both Ronald and I lost fish. "I hope I'm not in for a run of bad luck," I said.

"It does not matter quite so much here," said Uncle. "There are always plenty more ready to take."

"Why do they take so much better here?" asked Ronald.

"I think it is due to two things: one is that the fish are all fresh from the sea and have not had time to get stale, and two, these waters are so pure and unpolluted that the fish are fit during all their stay in the river. In Highland rivers so often there is a solution of peat in the water. This makes it acid and sickens the fish and you can't expect a fish that feels sick to take."

"Why are they so late in coming in Iceland?"

"Because of the ice," said Uncle. "In these Northern rivers the ice may remain till the middle of May and the drift ice on the coast till later still. The fish stay in these rivers for a shorter time for

the same reason. The rivers may freeze in early
November, so they have to spawn, and be away
as kelts, before the freeze-up, because if they don't
they never will get back to the sea."

We spent several days on the two top beats,
then one evening Gunnar said, " Why don't you
try the lower river?"

" Yes we must! What about some ponies for
to-morrow?" asked Uncle.

" That's all right, Gisli will have them ready
for you," was the reply.

Uncle told us that there were seven good pools
on the lowest beat and that the char would now
be in.

" What are char like?" asked Ronald.

" Well I hope you'll see to-morrow and seeing
them will give you a better idea than any descrip-
tion I can give, but they average about three
pounds. I have caught them up to eight pounds.
They are the same shape as a sea trout, but have
very small scales. When they first come from the
sea they are bright and silvery, but soon turn red,
not the rather muddy red of the salmon, but a
bright vermilion which looks lovely."

" Do they fight well?" I asked.

" Not all of them, but many do, and very often
I have thought that I was hooked to a salmon
only to find out later that it was a big char. They
are great fun and better takers than even the
salmon are here."

" Are they good to eat?" asked Ronald.

" Why can't you forget your stomach?" I asked.

Uncle laughed and said, " The Icelanders prefer them to nearly all other fishes. I think the first one is good, but I never want to eat more than one a season."

" What tackle do we want for them?"

" Just what you use for sea trout, but they take bigger flies, and I use the same flies as I do for salmon. I don't think the pattern matters; any fly size four will do."

The ride to the beat was good fun. The ponies were wonderful and very sure footed. I tried to take a short cut over some marshy ground, but my pony would not go that way. When Uncle saw what I was trying to do, he said, " Never make an Iceland pony go over bog, if he does not want to. These ponies know much better than you do what ground is safe for them to cross, and it's a waste of time getting you and the pony out if you get stuck."

When we got to the top of the beat we off-saddled and put hobbles on the ponies' fore-legs. If we had not done this they would have gone home and left us or refused to be caught again in the evening.

Uncle had brought two sacks for the fish. " Isn't that rather unlucky?" I asked.

" That's not my way of looking at it," said

Uncle. " If you came back here in the evening
with ten fish and had no sacks I'd call that unlucky. Fish are slimy, awkward things to carry
in your arms for ten miles."

The lower river is very different from the top
beats; here it runs through the coastal plain. The
land is flat, there are no rocks, the river bed is all
shingle, and the pools are long and deep. Also
the river has been made bigger by the addition of
two large tributaries. There are only seven pools,
but each pool is so long, that one man could
easily spend several hours fishing it.

There were swans, geese, ducks, divers, waders,
ravens, snipe and thousands of golden plover near
the river's mouth. All except the geese were very
tame. Of them all, I liked the little, ringed plover
best, and after them the dunlin.

We started fishing at the two top pools. Uncle
and Ronald went to the lower one.

Almost at once I hooked a big fish. He fought
like a wild cat and took me a long way down. I
shouted to Ronald, who in turn shouted to Uncle,
and they both came up to help. The water at the
tail of these lower river pools is very shallow and
we could see the fish nearly all the time. Even
where the breeze ruffled the surface, we could see
where he was by the great bow waves he made.

" He's huge," said Ronald.

" Yes, it's a good fish," said Uncle. Now
John, the water here is so shallow you'll have to

beach him, so when he's done, walk away from the edge and keep a steady strain on and you'll make him beach himself. This will be far quicker and safer than my trying to get near enough to gaff him, but I'll have the gaff ready in case the hold gives. Don't pull against him if he gets his head away from you, pull hardest when it's towards you or sideways on, and keep well back on the shingle yourself."

I did just what Uncle had told me and, after a long time, I got him into such shallow water that he lay on his side, then with each kick of his tail, he came a little further up the shingle and Uncle was able to tail him. He was a grand fish of $23\frac{1}{2}$ lbs.

"You played and landed that fish very well, John," said Uncle, and I felt rather pleased with the compliment, as well as with the fish.

"Always pick up a salmon by the tail. There is a bone in it and once you get a grip of it, the fish won't slip out of your hands, but don't try it on a grilse, a sea trout, or a char. In the case of the grilse the bone is not sufficiently developed to give you a grip and the other fish don't seem to have that bone at all."

It was Uncle who caught the first char, a lovely, little fish of about three pounds. When he got it ashore, beached in the same way as I had landed the salmon, he shouted, "Ronald, come and try here. You're certain to get something."

Ronald ran up and almost as soon as he put his fly in the water he rose a fish. It was not long before he had two char on the shingle.

I had gone back to my pool and caught two more salmon. They were not as big as the first fish: one was 13 lbs and the other a grilse of 5 lbs.

We finished that day with five salmon and fourteen char.

A few days after this we went to one of the lakes. There are no boats on it, so we had to fish from the shore, wading out as far as our waders would let us. Uncle warned us that there were soft places and to be careful, because it was a bad place in which to get stuck.

The trout in these lakes are very large—some of them up to four pounds—and they were easy to catch. They were seldom fished for and ready to take our flies. But the black flies were quite dreadful, far worse than our midges at home. There was no wind and these little insects came out in countless millions. I am not often driven off good water, but I had to stop fishing because of them. Fortunately, a breeze sprang up and drove them away. Uncle said that the only protection against them was a head net, but he complained, " With a net you can't smoke."

At three in the afternoon Uncle said, " Now don't you think we've caught enough? There's plenty of trout for all the local farms." So we stopped. I believe we could have caught as many more if we had gone on fishing.

The days flew by and almost before we had realized it our time was over. We went back to Reykjavik, had three days there, saw some of the wonderful sights and then sailed for home. Never, never will Ronald and I forget that holiday.

Chapter XXIV

HOW THE FISH SPAWN

THE Christmas holidays started early and we were home by 17th December. The winter had been very mild and the river was low. Uncle suggested that we go with Roderick and see the fish on the spawning redds, as it was easy to do this with the river at this height. So we arranged with Roderick to meet us at the bridge.

He took us about three miles up the river to a wide, shallow reach. Here the bed of the river is shingle. The stones were about the size of oranges and the water was only about five or six inches deep.

" Do you mean to say they lay their eggs in water as shallow as that," asked Ronald.

" Yes and sometimes even shallower. Do you see that heap of stones there?" pointing to a pile a few yards out from the shore. " Well, that is a redd; there were a pair of big fish there last week and that's their nest."

" I should have thought that they would have got dried out if the water gets any lower," I said.

" The salmon is not so stupid as that, although sometimes in a very hard frost, if it lasts a long time, the ova does get stranded."

" How do they move these stones?" I asked. " They seem too big for a fish to move."

" With their tails. There now, see yon fish? Ay there's his mate." And he pointed to a spot in the middle of the stream. Here the water was a little deeper, but Ronald and I saw the fish clearly. One seemed to be lying on its side and flopping its tail.

" That's the hen fish. She makes a trench that way, lying on her side so as to remain in one place. See the stones she's shifting." At that moment the other fish, which had been lying behind her, darted away.

" Oh! Look! He's just attacked another fish," said Ronald, and indeed he had, though the other fish did not stay to argue, but swam away as fast as he could.

" Ay! They're that jealous of each other at this time, but in three days he won't even remember which hen he mated with," said Roderick, " and the children will never know their mothers, which is perhaps as well as she may have over 10,000."

" Look, there's another pair, but the hen is five times as big as the cock. Why, that's only a grilse she's with," I said.

" Sometimes a full grown hen will even mate with a parr. Yes, and some of the eggs will be fertile. I've taken them and hatched them in the old hatchery," said Roderick.

" Why don't you do that now?" I asked.

" Because we find that they do it better themselves. Nature has a wonderful way with its own children and we can't improve on it."

I very much wanted to get close to a pair of spawning fish, but at this place it was not possible, so we went on up the river and at the mouth of a big burn we were able to see better. But Roderick said that it was easier to see the sea trout spawning as they went up the burns and it is possible to get within three feet of them. But by December all the sea trout had spawned.

" When you come for Easter I'll show you the alevins and fry," said Roderick, " just by that wee bridge, you can see them on any sunny day in April."

We came back to the first spawning place and were standing looking when Roderick shouted, " Och! the old devil! See that eel eating all the spawn." And sure enough behind the spawning pair was an eel fairly gobbling up the ova.

Roderick could not stand the sight of this, so picking up a large stone, he plunged into the shallow water and tried to stone it. He frightened the two salmon and the eel, but it got away.

" Will the salmon come back to that redd?" I asked.

" Yes, they won't mind. They'll be back in twenty minutes, but I must bring the wee rifle next time, ay! Many's the eel I've shot with it."

" But how do you shoot them in the water?"

" If they're far out you can't, but if you can get a bit above them you can stun them with the bullet and then it's easy to pick them up."

We went back to the house having learnt quite a lot.

. . . .

One evening shortly afterwards Uncle said, " You've both become fishermen of a sort and I cannot teach or tell you very much more. From now on, if you want to improve, it will have to be experience that teaches you. Soon now, both of you will be leaving school and you have your way to make in the world. So for a time, your opportunities for fishing may well be less than you've had in the school holidays. But you are both lovers of the game and in after years I hope that it will bring pleasure to you to remember that you have had the fun of the fishing here. I hope dearly that you will come back to me and that we will fish together again many times. But from now on you will be companions rather than pupils. We'll exchange experiences together and all three of us learn from each other. So to all young anglers and to you, John and Ronald—Tight Lines."